Cats
Sleep
Anywhere

Donna Alvermann
Connie A. Bridge
Barbara A. Schmidt
Lyndon W. Searfoss
Peter Winograd
Scott G. Paris

D.C. Heath and Company
HEATH Lexington, Massachusetts Toronto, Ontario

Acknowledgments

Grateful acknowledgment is made for permission to reprint the following copyrighted material.

Asch, Frank. "**Bear Shadow**," from *Bear Shadow*, by Frank Asch. Copyright © 1985 by Frank Asch. Used by permission of the publisher Prentice-Hall, Inc., Englewood Cliffs, N.J.

Belpré, Pura. "**Señor Billy Goat**," from *The Tiger and the Rabbit and Other Tales*, by Pura Belpré. Copyright 1944, 1946, by Pura Belpré. Reprinted by permission.

Bulla, Clyde Robert. "**What Makes a Shadow?**" abridged from *What Makes a Shadow?* by Clyde Robert Bulla (Thomas Y. Crowell). Text copyright © 1962 by Clyde Robert Bulla. Reprinted by permission of Harper & Row, Publishers, Inc.

Cole, William. "**The Only Place**," copyright © 1979 by William Cole, reprinted by permission of William Morrow & Co.

Domanska, Janina. **The Turnip**. Adapted with permission of Macmillan Publishing Company from *The Turnip*, by Janina Domanska. Copyright © 1969 by Janina Domanska.

Farjeon, Eleanor. "**Cats**" is reprinted by permission of Harold Ober Associates, Inc.

Guinness Book of World Records. "**What's So Big About That?**" is adapted by Meg Buckley from the *Guinness Book of World Records*, copyright © 1986 by Guinness Superlatives Ltd. Reprinted by permission of Sterling Publishing Company, Inc.

Hutchins, Pat. **Clocks and More Clocks**, copyright © 1970 by Pat Hutchins, reprinted by permission of Macmillan Publishing Company.

Leach, Maria. "**Why Cat Eats First and Washes Afterward**," from *The Lion Sneezed: Folktales and Myths of the Cat*, by Maria Leach (Thomas Y. Crowell Co.). Copyright © 1977 by Macdonald H. Leach. Reprinted by permission of Harper & Row, Publishers, Inc.

McGovern, Ann. **Too Much Noise**. Copyright © 1967 by Ann McGovern. Adapted by permission of the Author.

Moore, Lilian. "**Big/Little**," from *Little Raccoon and Poems from the Woods*, by Lilian Moore. Copyright © 1975 by Lilian Moore. Reprinted by permission of Marian Reiner for the Author.

Parish, Peggy. **Good Work, Amelia Bedelia**. Text copyright © 1976 by Margaret Parish. Illustrations copyright © 1976 by Lynn Sweat. By permission of Greenwillow Books (a division of William Morrow & Company).

Parish, Peggy. Condensation of **The Cats' Burglar**, by Peggy Parish. Copyright © 1983 by Margaret Parish. By permission of Greenwillow Books (a division of William Morrow & Company).

Prelutsky, Jack. "**Tick Tock Clock**," from *Rainy Rainy Saturday*, by Jack Prelutsky. Copyright © 1980 by Jack Prelutsky. By permission of Greenwillow Books (a division of William Morrow & Company).

Ross, Pat. **Molly and the Slow Teeth**, by Pat Ross. Copyright © 1980 by Pat Ross. Adapted by permission of Lothrop, Lee & Shepard Books (a division of William Morrow & Company).

Schneider, Herman, and Nina Schneider. "**Science Fun**," adapted from *Science Fun With a Flashlight*. Copyright © 1975 by Herman and Nina Schneider. Reprinted by permission of McGraw Hill Book Company.

Schwartz, Alvin. "**Tell a Joke**," adapted from *Tomfoolery: Trickery and Foolery With Words*, collected from American Folklore by Alvin Schwartz (J.B. Lippincott). Text copyright © 1973 by Alvin Schwartz. Reprinted by permission of Harper & Row, Publishers, Inc.

Sharmat, Marjorie Weinman. **Nate the Great and the Sticky Case**. Text copyright © 1978 by Marjorie Weinman Sharmat. Reprinted by permission of Coward, McCann & Geoghegan.

Weiss, Leatie. **Heather's Feathers**. Copyright © 1976 by Leatie Weiss. Reprinted by permission of Franklin Watts, Inc.

White, Anne Terry. "**The Lion and the Mouse**," adapted by permission of Random House, Inc., from *Aesop's Fables*, retold by Anne Terry White. Copyright © 1964 by Anne Terry White.

Yolen, Jane, and Tomie de Paola. "**Grizzle's Grumble**," from *The Giants' Farm*, by Jane Yolen, illustrated by Tomie de Paola. Copyright © 1976 by Jane Yolen. Copyright © 1976 by Tomie de Paola. Reprinted by permission of Clarion Books/Ticknor & Fields, a Houghton Mifflin Company.

Ziner, Feenie, and Elizabeth Thompson. "**Old Ways of Telling Time**," adapted from *Time*, copyright © 1982 by Feenie Ziner and Elizabeth Thompson. Reprinted by permission of Childrens Press.

Zolotow, Charlotte. "**Look**," from *All That Sunlight*, by Charlotte Zolotow. Text copyright © 1967 by Charlotte Zolotow. Reprinted by permission of Harper & Row, Publishers, Inc.

(Continued on page 255)

Table of Contents

2

Here, Kitty, Kitty

Let's Be Silly

3

Teeth Talk

A Big Help

Cats Sleep Anywhere

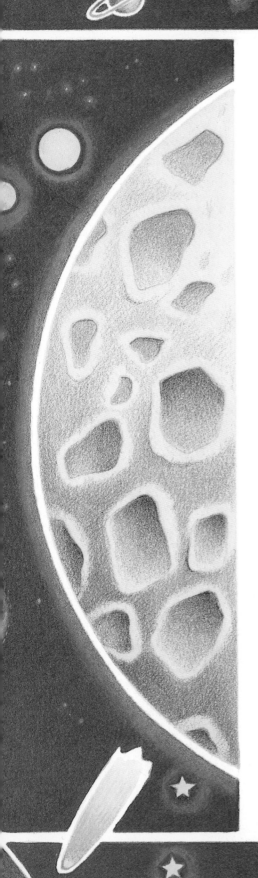

Think Big!

What are the biggest ants
in the world? (*giants*)

What grows bigger the more
you take from it? (*a hole*)

What is six feet long, green,
and has two tongues?
(*The Jolly Green Giant's sneakers*)

Grizzle's Grumble

modern fairy tale
from THE GIANTS' FARM *by Jane Yolen*

It was a gray day. The giants were all at home.

Grizzle began to grumble. No one listened to him. He grumbled louder. Still no one heard. At last he began to sing a grumbling song:

> "I do not like being big.
> I do not like being big.
> I fall and break things,
> I cannot make things,
> I do not like being big."

This time the other giants heard him.

"You are right," said Stout. "It is no fun being big. A big hand gets stuck in the cookie jar."

This made Grizzle even sadder. He
sang his grumble even louder.

> "I do not like being big.
> I do not like being big.
> Nothing fits right,
> Nothing sits right,
> I do not like being big."

"You are right," said Grab.

"You are right," said Grub.

Then Grab said, "If you are big, you get
all the hand-me-ups. Like the socks that
have lost their elastic."

Grub added, "And the sweaters that are all stretched out."

Grizzle felt sadder and sadder. His chin fell to his chest. His mouth pulled down. He tried to sing his grumble again. All that came out was:

"I do not . . . *blub* . . . *blub* . . . *blub*."

Little Dab came into the room. "I have a *big* problem."

"I have a *big* problem, too," said Grizzle. "And it's me." He began to *blub* . . . *blub* . . . *blub* again.

"My big problem is that I cannot reach the book I want. It is on the very top shelf," said Dab.

"I will get it," said Grab, but he could not reach.

"I will get it," said Grub, but he could not reach.

Stout wiped his mouth. "I would try to get it for you," he said, "but if Grab cannot get it and Grub cannot get it, then I cannot get it."

"Oh dear," said Dab. "This is a *bigger* problem than I thought."

Grizzle stopped crying. He looked at the high shelf where Dab was pointing. Then he got up. And up. And up. He got the book and handed it to Dab.

Dab smiled up at Grizzle. "I don't know what I would do without some really big friends," he said. "I can take care of the *little* problems myself. But for *big* problems, I need a friend."

Grizzle thought about that for a minute. Then he smiled.

The sun came out. It wasn't a gray day any more.

Think About It

1. List the things that Grizzle does not like about being big.
2. Why does he change his mind?
3. How does Grizzle's size help him do things Grab and Grub can't do?
4. How would you feel about your size if you were Grizzle?

Create and Share

Make up a smiling song like Grizzle's grumbling song and share it.

Explore

Read books about big animals. Use what you find out to make a big picture called *Giant Animals*.

Big/Little

Big
     is
     Me,
     watching an
     ant
     tug
     a dead
     bug
     to a distant
     ant hill,
     blades of grass away.

Little
     is
     Me,
     watching a
     bear
     lift a paw
     to
     scoop a
     bees' nest
     from a
     tree.

—Lilian Moore

The Turnip

*Russian folktale retold
by Janina Domanska*

Grandfather planted a turnip in his
garden. Grandmother watered it every
day. The turnip got bigger and bigger.
  "My turnip is beautiful!" cried
Grandfather.

"Ho! Ho!" laughed Grandmother. "It's not your turnip. It's my turnip. Didn't I water it every day?"

"Ho! Ho!" shouted Grandfather. "I planted it, didn't I? So it's my turnip."

The turnip grew bigger. One morning Grandmother woke up before anyone else. "I will pull that turnip before the birds eat it," she said as she hurried to the garden.

She pulled and she pulled until she couldn't pull any more. But the turnip did not move.

The next morning Grandfather made up his mind to pull the turnip to surprise Grandmother. "It is so big," he thought. "Our neighbor's silly goat will start eating it." Grandfather pulled and pulled until he could not pull any more. But the turnip did not move.

Then Grandfather called Grandmother to help him pull the turnip. Grandmother came running. She was pleased that Grandfather had asked her to help him pull.

"We will pull *our* turnip!" she cried. They pulled and pulled. But the turnip did not move.

Grandfather wiped the sweat from his
brow. "Call Micky to help us," he said.

Micky, their grandson, came and they
all pulled. They puffed and they pulled
until they could not pull any more. But the
turnip did not move.

"Get the dog to help," said Grandfather
when he had his breath back.

The dog came and pulled at Micky.
They all pulled and pulled and pulled
until they could not pull any more. But
the turnip did not move.

Then the cat came and pulled behind the dog. And they all pulled and pulled. They puffed and pulled. But the turnip did not move.

Then the geese came to help and they made a goose chain. They pulled with the others. And they all pulled and they pulled and they pulled. But the turnip would not move.

"This big turnip is laughing at us!" shouted Grandfather, wiping the sweat from his brow. "Get the rooster and the hen. They can pull."

The rooster and the hen came and
pulled behind the geese.

"Now all together!" shouted Grandfather.
"One . . . two . . . three . . . *pull!*"

The rooster and the hen pulled at the
geese, who pulled at the cat, who pulled at
the dog, who pulled at Micky, who pulled
at Grandmother, who pulled at
Grandfather, who pulled at the turnip.

And they pulled and they puffed and
they pulled and they pulled. But the
turnip did not move.

Now just the pig was not pulling. He
was a very big, fat pig.

Grandfather shouted, "Get the pig!
Make him pull with us!"

The pig came and pulled at the hen.

"All together now," shouted Grandfather.
"One . . . two . . . three . . . *pull!*"
So they pulled and they panted. They
pulled and they pulled and pulled. But
the turnip did not move.

Grandfather wiped the sweat from his
brow. "No old turnip is going to beat me,"
he growled. "We will try again. Now all
at once." Grandfather shouted, "One . . .
two . . . three . . . *pull!*"

And they all pulled and they pulled and
they pulled. Soon they were all out of
breath. But the turnip did not move.

Grandfather wiped some more sweat
from his brow. "We will try once
more—and all of you pull."

"And that means you too!" they all
yelled to the pig. The pig took such a big
breath that he almost blew the curl out of
his tail. Then the pig got ready to pull
with the others again.

Just as Grandfather was about to tell
them all to pull at the turnip, a bird flew
down to help. The bird pulled at the
pig's tail.

"Now all at once!" cried Grandfather.

And they all pulled with all their might. They pulled and they pulled and they pulled. At once there was a loud noise and the turnip came out of the ground so suddenly that they all fell down.

"Oh, my!" called the bird. "Look what I have done." And he flew away to his tall tree. From there he watched them all lying flat on the grass. Grandfather sat and the big turnip rested in his arms.

Think About It

1. How did Grandfather and Grandmother finally get the turnip out?
2. The bird felt he got the turnip out of the ground. What do you think?
3. What did the problem with the turnip teach Grandmother and Grandfather?
4. Grizzle is a big helper, and the bird is a little helper. What does this tell you about size and helping?
5. Tell about a time you needed help.

Create and Share

Work with a friend to make cutouts of all the people in the story. Read the story aloud while a friend acts it out.

Explore

Watch a TV story about someone helping others. Write about what you saw.

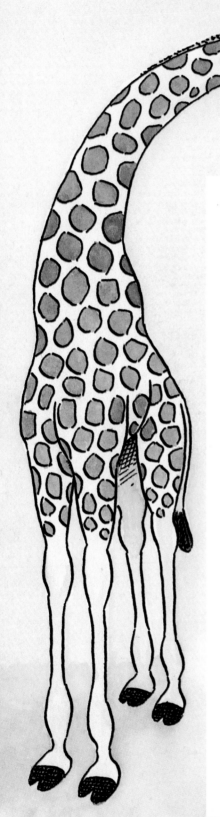

What's So Big About That?

from the GUINNESS BOOK OF WORLD RECORDS
adapted by Meg Buckley

Lots of people like to read about the biggest things in the world. They like to hear about surprising facts. There is a book that tells about all kinds of surprising facts. The book is called the *Guinness Book of World Records*. Here are some of its really big facts.

The tallest living animal is the giraffe. George, a giraffe at the Chester Zoo in England, was almost 20 feet high. Think how long his neck was!

The heaviest dog was a Saint Bernard. It weighed 310 pounds. That's more than a baby elephant weighs.

The redwood is the tallest tree. One of these trees grew to be 435 feet high. That is as high as 12 telephone poles!

What was the largest pumpkin ever grown? A man in Washington grew a pumpkin that weighed 612 pounds. That's about as heavy as 12 second graders.

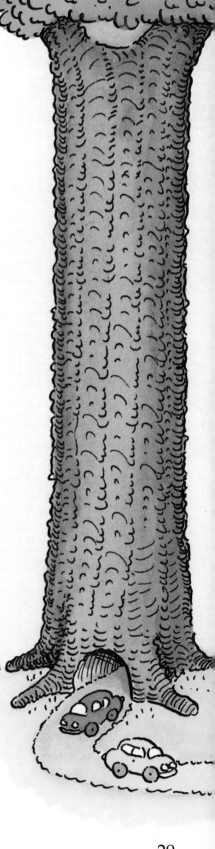

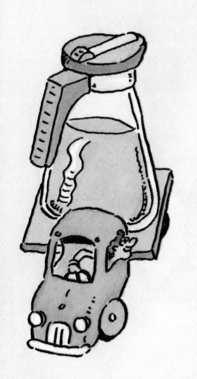

The largest pancake ever made was 20 feet across and 4 inches thick. It weighed over 2,000 pounds. The cooks had to use a helicopter and a crane to flip it over.

The people who made the pancake wanted to make something big. Lots of people look for ways to do something big. Other times people just find things that are the biggest of their kind. Look around you. Can you find something big enough for the *Guinness Book of World Records*?

Think About It

1. What new facts would you want to tell others about?
2. Why do people want to set world records?
3. What things do you know of that might be big enough for the *Guinness Book of World Records?*
4. How are things in this story like the giants in "Grizzle's Grumble" and the turnip in "The Turnip"?

Create and Share

What is the biggest thing you have ever seen? Write some facts about it for the *Guinness Book of World Records.*

Explore

Read some more facts in the *Guinness Book of World Records.*

Me and My Shadow

Firelight and shadows
dancing on the wall.
Look at my shadow
TEN FEET TALL!

LOOK *by Charlotte Zolotow*

What Makes a Shadow?

by Clyde Robert Bulla

The sun is shining. It shines on the trees and the sidewalk. It shines on your house. It shines on you, too.

When the sun is in front of you, look behind you. You can see your shadow. When you move, your shadow moves. When you run, your shadow runs, but you can never catch it.

What makes the shadow? Where does it come from? The sun is very bright. It shines on you, but it does not shine through you. There is a dark place behind you where the sun does not shine. The darkness is your shadow.

A tree has a shadow. The shade of the tree is the shadow of the tree. A house has a shadow. When the sun shines on one side of the house, there is a shadow on the other side.

A cloud has a shadow. Sometimes the sky is dark with clouds and the sun cannot shine through them. The shadows of the clouds fall on the earth. The shadows make the day dark. We say, "This is a cloudy day."

Night is a shadow. When the sun shines on one side of the earth, the other side is in a shadow. The shadow makes the night. Night is the biggest shadow of all.

Think About It

1. What makes a shadow?
2. What happens when the sky is cloudy and the sun cannot shine through the clouds?
3. Why is night the biggest shadow of all?
4. When the sun shines on the front of your house, where will you see the shadow of the house?

Create and Share

Fold your paper in three parts. Draw your shadow on a sunny day, a cloudy day, and a rainy day.

Explore

Read to find out what kind of shadow an eclipse is.

Bear Shadow

by Frank Asch

One day Bear went down to the pond
with his fishing pole and a big can of
worms. While he was putting a worm on
his hook, he looked down and saw a big
fish. I'm going to catch that fish, thought
Bear to himself. But when Bear stood up
to throw his line in the water, his shadow
scared the big fish away.

"Go away, Shadow!" cried Bear.

But Bear's shadow would not go away.

"All right," said Bear. "If you won't go on your own, then I'll just have to get rid of you!"

And he put down his fishing pole and began to run. He ran around the pond. When he got to the other side he kept on running. He ran through a field of flowers, jumped over the brook, and hid behind a tree.

"Good!" thought Bear. "Now Shadow can't find me."

But Bear was wrong. When he stepped out from behind the tree, the first thing he saw was Shadow.

Nearby was a cliff. Bear walked over to the cliff and looked up. I'll climb so high Shadow won't be able to follow me, thought Bear. Bear climbed higher and higher until at last he pulled himself up to the top. Huffing and puffing, he smiled with pride. Then he looked down and saw Shadow.

Now Bear was very upset, so he went home and got a hammer and some nails to nail his shadow to the ground. He hammered and hammered and hammered, but he couldn't nail his shadow down.

If I can't nail him down, thought Bear, maybe I can bury him. So he got his shovel and dug a hole. When the hole was deep and wide, he let his shadow fall in the hole. Then Bear filled in the hole with dirt. When he was done it was almost noon. The sun was high in the sky and Shadow was nowhere to be seen.

"At last!" sighed Bear. "No more shadow!"

But now Bear was very tired. So he went inside and took a little nap. While he slept, time passed and the sun once again cast shadows everywhere. When Bear got up and opened his door, he saw his shadow on the floor.

"Not you again!" yelled Bear. And he slammed the door, hoping to lock Shadow inside. But Shadow was too quick.

"Mmm," sighed Bear, "how about this? If you let me catch a fish, I'll let you catch one, too. Nod your head like this if it's a deal."

When Bear nodded his head, Shadow nodded, too. So Bear went back to the pond and once again threw his line in the water. By this time the sun was in a different part of the sky, which made it easy for Shadow to keep his part of the deal. And when Bear caught that big fish, Shadow caught one, too.

Think About It

1. Tell about all the ways Bear tries to get rid of Shadow.
2. What happens to your shadow when it's dark out?
3. List the best times to go fishing without your shadow.
4. How do you think Bear's ideas might change if he read the story "What Makes a Shadow?"

Create and Share

Write what you would tell Bear to help him understand shadows. Draw a picture to go with what you write.

Explore

Hold a flashlight over a stick. Move the flashlight to the left and right. Look at each shadow. Tell what happens.

Science Fun

from SCIENCE FUN WITH A FLASHLIGHT
by Herman and Nina Schneider

Shadows come in many sizes and shapes. They can be long or short. They can be fuzzy or sharp.

Here are some ways to make different kinds of shadows.

Shadows

Light shines out of your flashlight. A circle of light shines on the wall. Your hand stops some of the light, so a part of the circle is dark. This dark part is a shadow. The shadow of a hand looks like a hand. Can the shadow of a hand look like anything else?

Animal Shadows

A hand in the light makes a duck in the dark. Try for a rabbit. Can you wiggle his ears?

Long and Short Shadows

In the morning, the sun is low in the sky. The sunlight comes at a slant. The shadows are long. As the sun gets higher and higher in the sky, the slant of the sunlight changes. Guess how the shadows will change.

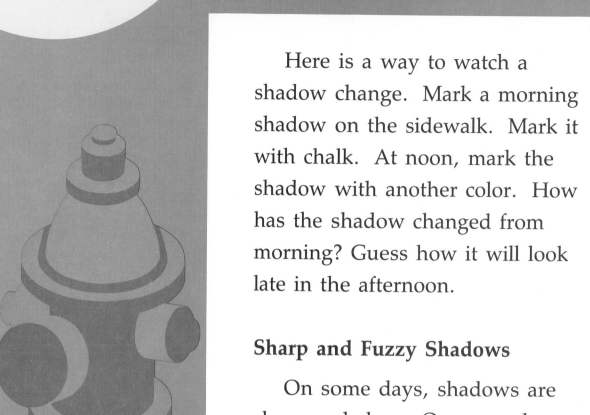

Here is a way to watch a shadow change. Mark a morning shadow on the sidewalk. Mark it with chalk. At noon, mark the shadow with another color. How has the shadow changed from morning? Guess how it will look late in the afternoon.

Sharp and Fuzzy Shadows

On some days, shadows are sharp and clear. On some days, shadows are fuzzy. What makes the shadow look fuzzy? Make a shadow like a bear.

See how sharp and clear it is. The dark parts are quite dark. The light parts around the shadow are quite light.

Now put wax paper over the flashlight. How do the light parts around the shadow change? The wax paper makes the shadow fuzzy.

The same thing happens in sunlight. Sometimes clouds get in the way of sunlight. The clouds change the shadows like the wax paper did. Thin clouds make shadows fuzzy.

On a very cloudy day, there are no shadows at all. Show somebody how this happens. Use some wax paper. Fold it over and over. What happens to the shadow as the wax paper gets thicker and thicker?

Now that you know how shadows are made and change, you can create your own fun with shadows.

Think About It

1. When is your shadow the longest?
2. How can you make shadows change?
3. What else could you use to make animal shadows?
4. Think about the two stories "What Makes a Shadow?" and "Science Fun." Which story could help Bear more? Tell why you think so.

Create and Share

Make an animal shadow with your hand or with a paper shape. Tell a story with your animal shadow.

Explore

You know how wax paper can change a shadow. Try putting other kinds of paper over a flashlight. Write how each kind of paper changes the shadow.

Drakestail

French fairy tale retold by Cynthia C. Nye

Drakestail, a duck
King
Fox
Ladder
River
Wasps
Servant
Chickens
Crowd

Scene One

(**Drakestail** *is sitting on a rock, counting.*)

Drakestail: Fifty, fifty-one, fifty-two, fifty-three. Now I have fifty-three gold coins.

(**King** *walks up to Drakestail*.)

King: Drakestail! Drakestail!

Drakestail: *(Surprised)* Oh my, it's the king!
Come in, King.

King: I hear that you have some money.
Will you let me take it? I will pay you
back very soon.

Drakestail: I have fifty-three gold coins.
I will let you take fifty of my coins.

(**Drakestail** *gives his coins to King*.)

King: Thank you, Drakestail. I will come
back soon.

Scene Two

(Two years later)

Drakestail: I have waited for two years. The king has not come back. I cannot wait any more. I will go to see the king.

(**Drakestail** *walks to King's castle.*)

Drakestail: Quack, quack, quack! When will I get my money back?

(**Drakestail** *stops walking when he sees Fox coming.*)

Fox: Good morning, Drakestail. Where are you going today?

Drakestail: I am going to the king to get my money.

Fox: Oh, take me with you!

Drakestail: One cannot have too many friends. You may go with me. Make yourself very small and jump into my pocket.

(**Fox** *jumps into Drakestail's pocket. Then* **Drakestail** *starts walking again.*)

Drakestail: Quack, quack, quack! When will I get my money back?

(**Drakestail** *stops by Ladder.*)

Drakestail: Good morning, Ladder!
Ladder: Good morning, Drakestail. Where are you going today?
Drakestail: I am going to the king to get my money.
Ladder: Oh, take me with you!

Drakestail: One cannot have too many
friends. You may go with me. Make
yourself very small and jump into my
pocket.

(**Ladder** *jumps into Drakestail's pocket.*)

Drakestail: Quack, quack, quack! When
will I get my money back?

(**Drakestail** *walks until he sees River.*)

Drakestail: Good morning, River!
River: Good morning, Drakestail. Where
are you going today?

Drakestail: I am going to the king to get my money.

River: Oh, take me with you!

Drakestail: One cannot have too many friends. You may go with me. Make yourself very small and get into my pocket.

(**River** *jumps into Drakestail's pocket.*)

Drakestail: Quack, quack, quack! When will I get my money back?

(**Drakestail** *walks on and meets up with Wasps.*)

Drakestail: Good morning, Wasps!

Wasps: Good morning, Drakestail. Where are you going today?

Drakestail: I am going to the king to get my money.

Wasps: Oh, take us with you!

Drakestail: One cannot have too many friends. You may go with me. Make yourselves very small and fly into my pocket.

(**Wasps** *fly into Drakestail's pocket.*)

Scene Three

(**Drakestail** *is now at King's gate. He sees Servant.*)

Drakestail: Quack, quack, quack! I want my money back!

Servant: Who is at the gate?

Drakestail: It is Drakestail. I want to talk to the king.

Servant: (*Gruffly*) The king cannot talk to you now. He is eating his lunch.

Drakestail: Please tell him that I am here.

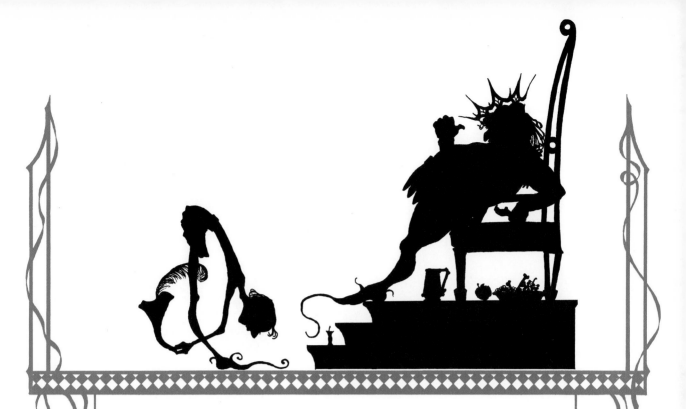

(**Servant** *goes to King.*)

Servant: Drakestail is at the gate and wants
to talk to you. Do you know who he is?

King: Yes, I know who Drakestail is. Let
him come inside the gate. Then put
him with the chickens.

(**Servant** *goes back to Drakestail.*)

Servant: Come this way to see the king.

(**Servant** *leads Drakestail to the henhouse.*
He pushes Drakestail in with the chickens.)

Drakestail: Why am I left with the
chickens? I do not like this. Quack!
Quack! Quack! When will I get my
money back?

(**Chickens** *start crowding around Drakestail.*)

Chickens: Cluck, cluck, cluck. Get out!
Get out!

Drakestail: Dear Fox, please come and
help me!

(**Fox** *jumps out of Drakestail's pocket and goes
after Chickens.* **Chickens** *fly away.*)

Chickens: Cluck! Cluck! Cluck! Help!
We see a fox! Help, help!

(**Drakestail** *and* **Fox** *leave the henhouse.*
King *comes by with Servant.*)

King: What is that noise?
Servant: Drakestail has frightened the
chickens.
King: Put Drakestail into the well.

(**King** *leaves as Drakestail enters.*
Servant *pushes Drakestail into the well.*)

Drakestail: Oh, how will I ever get out of this well? Dear Ladder, please come and help me.

(*Up comes* **Ladder** *and* **Drakestail** *climbs out of the well.*)

Drakestail: Quack, quack, quack! When will I get my money back?

King: (*whispering to Servant*) Put Drakestail into the fire.

(**Servant** *pushes Drakestail toward the fire.*)

Drakestail: River, please come and
help me!

(**River** *rushes out of Drakestail's pocket and
puts out the fire.*)

King: *(Angrily)* Bring Drakestail to me!

(**Servant** *takes Drakestail to King.*)

Drakestail: Oh, dear, what shall I do now?
Dear Wasps, please come and help me.

(**Wasps** *fly out of Drakestail's pocket. They go
after King.*)

Wasps: Buzz, buzz, buzz!

(**Wasps** *chase King and Servant away.*)

Drakestail: I am very tired. I will rest a little while on the king's throne. Then I will go home.

(*While* **Drakestail** *rests on the throne,* **Crowd** *comes into the room.*)

Crowd: Drakestail, we all think you are very brave and very smart. You shall be our new king.

Drakestail: Quack, quack, quack. Now I have my money back.

Think About It

1. Why did Drakestail visit the king?
2. Why didn't the king want to see Drakestail?
3. Drakestail said, "One cannot have too many friends." How did this turn out to be true?
4. Do you think Drakestail will be a good king? Tell why or why not.

Create and Share

Share what you would say if you were the king and Drakestail came to you.

Explore

Find out different ways you can make shadow puppets and a stage.

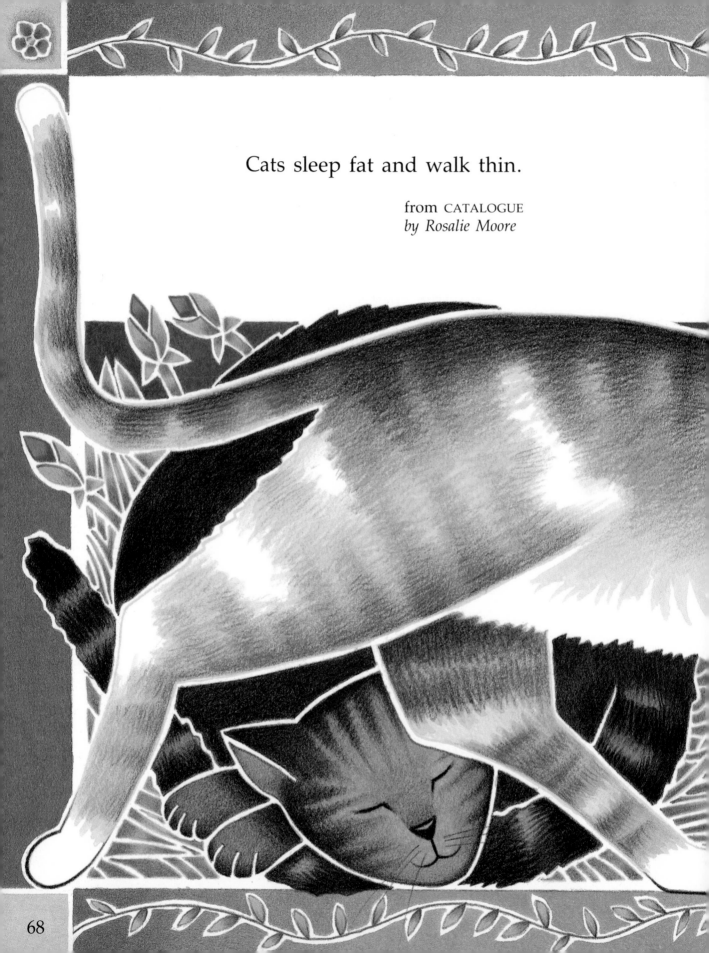

Cats sleep fat and walk thin.

from CATALOGUE
by Rosalie Moore

Here, Kitty, Kitty

CATS

Cats sleep
Anywhere,
Any table,
Any chair,
Top of piano,
Window-ledge,
In the middle,
On the edge,
Open drawer,
Empty shoe,
Anybody's
Lap will do,
Fitted in a
Cardboard box,
In the cupboard
With your frocks—
Anywhere!
They don't care!
Cats sleep
Anywhere.

—*Eleanor Farjeon*

The Cats' Burglar

by Peggy Parish

"Oh, Aunt Emma," said Mrs. James. "Not another cat!"

"Isn't he cute?" said Aunt Emma. "I named him Baby Bear."

Mr. James looked around. Cats were here, there, everywhere.

"Look at them," he said. "They are ripping up everything."

"I don't care," said Aunt Emma. "Everything is old anyway. I like to see them play. They make me laugh."

"You have too many cats," said Miss Wilson. "People are laughing at you."

"Oh, shush," said Aunt Emma. "I'm an old lady. I don't care what people say."

She looked at the clock. "My goodness," she said. "It is my bedtime. All of you, shoo."

Aunt Emma's friends left.

"I will see you tomorrow," she called.

"Have a good night," called Mr. James.

Aunt Emma went into her bedroom. The cats went with her. Then Aunt Emma got into bed.

"Good night, cats," she said.

The cats lay down here, there, everywhere. Soon everyone was asleep.

Suddenly, cats jumped onto Aunt Emma's bed. She sat up.

"What—what!" she said.

The cats were very quiet. They listened. Aunt Emma listened, too. She heard a noise. She did not know what made the noise.

Then she heard another noise. *ACHOO!* She knew what made that noise.

"Oh, my goodness!" said Aunt Emma. "Someone is in my house."

Quietly she got up. Quietly she closed her bedroom door. She locked it. Aunt Emma called the police.

"This is Aunt Emma," she said. "A burglar is in my house."

"We will come right over," said Chief Dan.

Aunt Emma hung up the telephone.

"Thank you, cats," she said. "Are you all here?"

She put on her light.

"One, two, three, four, five, six, seven, eight," she counted. "Someone is missing."

She looked at the cats.

"Baby Bear!" said Aunt Emma.

She looked around the room. There was no Baby Bear.

"What should I do?" said Aunt Emma.

ACHOO! The cats jumped. Aunt Emma jumped, too.

"Burglar or not," she said, "I must find Baby Bear."

Quietly she opened her door. Quietly she walked out. Quietly the cats went with her. Aunt Emma saw a dim light. She saw a burglar. And she saw Baby Bear.

"*Achoo!* Go away, cat!" said the burglar. "*Achoo!* Go away!"

Baby Bear wanted to play. He wanted the burglar to play. Aunt Emma smiled. She put on the light.

The burglar jumped. Baby Bear jumped, too. He jumped on the burglar's leg.

"Ouch! *Achoo!*" said the burglar.
"*Achoo!* Get down! *Achoo!*"

Aunt Emma stared at the burglar.

"Oh, my goodness!" she said.

Scruffy stared, too. The burglar wore a
hat. The hat had a feather. Scruffy wanted
that feather. He took a big jump. He
landed on the burglar.

One by one the other cats jumped on
the burglar.

"*ACHOO!*" sneezed the burglar. "Get
them off! *Achoo!* I can't—*achoo*—move."

But the burglar did move. He began to shake. The cats clung to him. They were having fun.

Aunt Emma tried not to laugh, but she had to.

Just then she heard the police car.

Aunt Emma ran to open the door. The cats ran to hide. The police chief ran into the house.

"Aunt Emma!" said Chief Dan. "Are you all right?"

Aunt Emma nodded her head. She couldn't talk. She was laughing too hard.

"*Achoo!* Please save me!" yelled the burglar. "I will—*achoo*—never—*achoo*—steal again."

Aunt Emma laughed. "That was so funny," she said.

"No," said Chief Dan. "Burglars are never funny."

"You are right," said Aunt Emma. "I was very lucky. My cats saved me."

"Thank you, cats," Chief Dan said. He took the burglar away.

The next day, all of the neighbors came to visit.

"Now what do you think?" said Aunt Emma. "Do I have too many cats?"

"Indeed not!" said Mr. James.

Think About It

1. How are the cats in the poem like Aunt Emma's cats?
2. Why do Aunt Emma's neighbors change their minds about all her cats?
3. Do you think the burglar will ever steal again? Why or why not?
4. Do you know any pets who have helped people? Tell about them.

Create and Share

Make a picture of one of the cats in the poem. Show where it is sleeping.
Name your picture *Cat sleeps* _____.

Explore

Talk to five people who have cats for pets.
Make a list of all the places their cats sleep.

Why Cat Eats First and Washes Afterward

by Maria Leach

One day Cat caught a fine mouse and was just about to eat it when Mouse said, "You have no manners! Don't you wash your face and hands before you eat?"

Cat felt bad, so she began to lick her paws and wash her face.

While Cat was washing, Mouse ran off and never came back.

Ever since, Cat eats first and washes her face and paws afterward.

Cat Habits

by Laura Tills

Have you ever had a cat say "I like you" in cat talk? Did you ever find your cat sleeping in your favorite chair? If you have, then you know that cats are special pets. Cats have their own way of doing things. You can be good friends with your cat if you understand its habits.

Cats talk to people in many ways. A cat will purr if it is happy. A cat will hiss if it is angry. Other times, it tells you things with its body. If a cat arches its back, it might be angry or afraid. By turning over on its back, a cat may be asking for a belly scratch. When you are not looking, a cat may give you a kiss with its nose.

Cats have fussy eating habits. They eat only food they like, but they do not eat too much. When cats are full, they save their food for a snack later on.

When a cat wants to play, watch out! If you are sweeping the floor, a cat may try to grab the broom. Cats like to play with anything that swings or moves. Cats also like to sniff and roll in catnip. Sometimes cats like to climb to high places. Then they jump. If a cat climbs too high, it may want you to come up and get it.

Cats sleep a lot. They like warm places. They sleep in spots that are sunny. Sometimes they will sleep under a lamp. Cats like soft places too. They may curl up in a favorite chair or pillow.

All these habits make cats special pets. If you know your cat's habits, you can be a good friend to it. Then your cat will be a good friend to you too.

Think About It

1. In "Why Cat Eats First and Washes Afterward," what does Cat learn from Mouse?
2. What does "Cat Habits" tell you about the sleeping habits of cats that the poem "Cats" doesn't?
3. What are some things a cat tells you with its body?
4. What did you find out about cats that you did not know before?

Create and Share

Bring in pictures of your cat or look for pictures of cats with funny habits. Talk about the pictures.

Explore

Read some *Curious George* books. Write down some of George's habits.

Follow Your Nose

by Linda Leopold Strauss

Jody wanted to play, but his friends
were not home that morning.

"Go for a walk," said Mother. "Just be
back by lunchtime because we are having
a cookout."

"Where should I go?" Jody said.

"A walk is a walk," said Mother. "Just follow your nose."

Jody started down the street. Near the end of the block he saw a worm on the sidewalk and put it on the grass. Jody liked rescuing worms. He watched the worm wiggle its way into the ground before he started walking again.

"Follow your nose," his mother had
said. Jody noticed some birds scolding
around a tall maple tree. He wondered
why the birds were so upset. The maple
tree was too high for Jody to climb, but
there was a good climbing tree nearby.
Jody went to the smaller tree and followed
his nose up a few branches. To his
surprise there was a boy in the tree. Jody
had never seen him before.

"Do you know what the birds are mad at?" Jody asked the boy, who said his name was Tomás.

"It's my kitten," he told Jody. "A dog chased her onto that high branch over there. I thought I could get her from here, but I can't reach that far."

Looking across to the maple tree, Jody saw a little black and white kitten clinging to the thin end of a high branch. The branch swayed.

"Be careful, Panda!" Tomás cried.

The kitten looked across and meowed.

"She can't get to you," Jody said. "Cats can't jump from tree to tree like squirrels."

"I know," said Tomás, "but what am I going to do?"

Jody thought the kitten could get down if she went back to the tree trunk.

"Follow me," he told Tomás. He climbed down to the ground with Tomás after him.

"Now stand here," he told Tomás. "And call the kitten softly."

"Panda," called Tomás.

"Keep calling and move this way," Jody said.

Jody led Tomás closer and closer to the trunk of the maple tree. The kitten followed on the branch above. When Panda got to the tree trunk, the boys knew she would make it down the rest of the way.

"Thanks," said Tomás to Jody. He looked up into the maple tree. "Now come down, Panda," he scolded.

"It's easy, Panda," Jody called up. "Just follow your nose."

But Panda had her own ideas. She was coming down backwards. She turned and held on. Then she slid and skittered down the big tree trunk as Jody and Tomás watched.

"Her nose followed *her*," Tomás giggled, scooping the kitten up in his arms. "At least she's safe."

Tomás told Jody he would be moving into the new house at the end of the block. Jody was glad. He felt good that he had helped Tomás.

On just one walk he had rescued a worm, saved a kitten, and made a friend. Now it was lunchtime and time to say good-bye. His mother had started the cookout. Jody could smell it. He sniffed at the air hungrily and headed home, following his nose.

Think About It

1. What do you think of Mother's idea that Jody follow his nose?
2. Tell what else Tomás could have done to get Panda down from the tree.
3. Tell why you would like to have Jody as a friend.
4. In what ways is this story like "The Cats' Burglar"?

Create and Share

Draw a map. Show the places that Jody went as he followed his nose. Use the map to help you tell the story.

Explore

Use your nose at lunchtime. Make a list of all the foods around you that you can tell just by their smell.

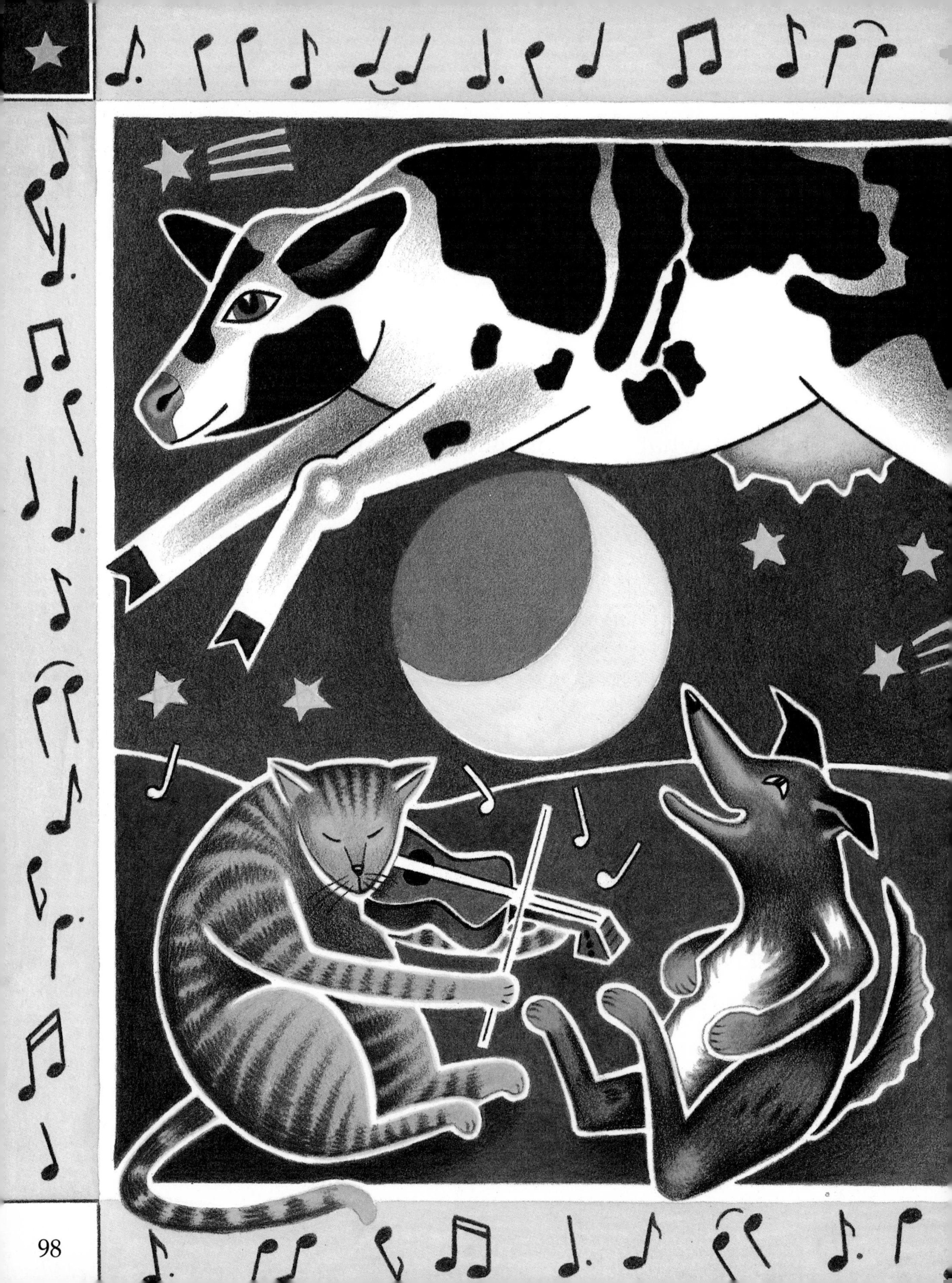

Let's Be Silly

Hey diddle diddle,
The cat and the fiddle,
The cow jumped over the moon.
The little dog laughed
To see such sport,
And the dish ran away
   with the spoon.

Mother Goose

Too Much Noise

traditional folktale retold by Ann McGovern

Storyteller	Cow	Hen
Peter	Donkey	Dog
Wise man	Sheep	Cat

Storyteller: A long time ago there was an old man. His name was Peter, and he lived in an old, old house. The bed creaked. The floor squeaked. Outside, the wind blew the leaves through the trees. The leaves fell on the roof. (*Swish. Swish.*) The tea kettle whistled. (*Hiss. Hiss.*)

Peter: Too noisy.

Storyteller: Peter went to see the wise man of the village.

Peter: What can I do? My house makes too much noise. My bed creaks. My floor squeaks. The wind blows the leaves through the trees. The leaves fall on the roof. (*Swish. Swish.*) My tea kettle whistles. (*Hiss. Hiss.*)

Wise man: I can help you. I know what you can do.

Peter: What?

Wise man: Get a cow.

Peter: What good is a cow?

Storyteller: But Peter got a cow anyhow.

Cow: Moo. MOO.

Storyteller: The bed creaked. The floor squeaked. The leaves fell on the roof. (*Swish. Swish.*) The tea kettle whistled. (*Hiss. Hiss.*)

Peter: Too noisy.

Storyteller: Peter went back to the wise man.

Wise man: Get a donkey.

Peter: What good is a donkey?

Storyteller: But Peter got a donkey anyhow.

Donkey: HEE-Haw.

Cow: Moo. MOO.

Storyteller: The bed creaked. The floor squeaked. The leaves fell on the roof. (*Swish. Swish.*) The tea kettle whistled. (*Hiss. Hiss.*)

Peter: Still too noisy.

Storyteller: And Peter went back to the wise man again.

Wise man: Get a sheep.

Peter: What good is a sheep?

Storyteller: But Peter got a sheep anyhow.

Sheep: Baa. Baa.

Donkey: HEE-Haw.

Cow: Moo. MOO.

Storyteller: The bed creaked. The floor
squeaked. The leaves fell on the roof.
(*Swish. Swish.*) The tea kettle whistled.
(*Hiss. Hiss.*)

Peter: Too noisy.

Storyteller: And he went back to the wise man.

Wise man: Get a hen.

Peter: What good is a hen?

Storyteller: But Peter got a hen anyhow.

Hen: Cluck. Cluck.

Sheep: Baa. Baa.

Donkey: HEE-Haw.

Cow: Moo. MOO.

Storyteller: The bed creaked. The floor squeaked. The leaves fell on the roof. (*Swish. Swish.*) The tea kettle whistled. (*Hiss. Hiss.*)

Peter: Too noisy.

Storyteller: And back he went to the wise man.

Wise man: Get a dog. And get a cat too.

Peter: What good is a dog? Or a cat?

Storyteller: But Peter got a dog and a cat anyhow.

Dog: Woof. Woof.

Cat: Mee-ow. Mee-ow.

Hen: Cluck. Cluck.

Sheep: Baa. Baa.

Donkey: HEE-Haw.

Cow: Moo. MOO.

Storyteller: The bed creaked. The floor squeaked. The leaves fell on the roof. (*Swish. Swish.*) The tea kettle whistled. (*Hiss. Hiss.*) Now Peter was angry. He went to the wise man.

Peter: I told you my house was too noisy. I told you my bed creaks. My floor squeaks. The leaves fall on the roof. (*Swish. Swish.*) The tea kettle whistles. (*Hiss. Hiss.*) You told me to get a cow. All day the cow says, "Moo. MOO." You told me to get a donkey. All day the donkey says, "HEE-Haw." You told me to get a sheep. All day the sheep says, "Baa. Baa." You told me to get a hen. All day the hen says, "Cluck. Cluck." You told me to get a dog. And a cat. All day the dog says, "Woof. Woof." All day the cat says, "Mee-ow. Mee-ow." I am going crazy.

Wise man: Do what I tell you. Let the cow go. Let the donkey go. Let the sheep go. Let the hen go. Let the dog go. Let the cat go.

Storyteller: So Peter let the cow go. He let the donkey go. He let the sheep go. He let the hen go. He let the dog go. He let the cat go. Now no cow said, "Moo. MOO." No donkey said, "HEE-Haw." No sheep said, "Baa. Baa." No hen said, "Cluck. Cluck." No dog said, "Woof. Woof." No cat said, "Mee-ow. Mee-ow." Only the bed creaked.

Peter: Ah, what a quiet noise.

Storyteller: The floor squeaked.

Peter: Oh, what a quiet noise.

Storyteller: Outside the leaves fell on the roof. (*Swish. Swish.*) Inside the tea kettle whistled. (*Hiss. Hiss.*)

Peter: Ah. Oh. How quiet my house is.

Storyteller: And Peter got into his bed and went to sleep and dreamed a very quiet dream.

Think About It

1. What were some things that made noise in Peter's house?
2. What happened when Peter let all of the animals go?
3. Why didn't the house noises seem too noisy to Peter at the end of the story?
4. If you were the wise man, what would you tell Peter to do?

Create and Share

Make name tags for all the people and animals in the play. Then choose parts and act out the play.

Explore

Look in the newspaper for comic strips about people doing silly things. Cut them out and make a book.

Tell a Joke

To tell the jokes on these pages, you will need a friend. For each line, you read the part in black, and have your friend read the part in red.

I want to tell you a story. To help me, you must say "Just like me" each time I stop. Okay.

I went up one flight of stairs.	Just like me.
I went up two flights of stairs.	Just like me.
I went up three flights of stairs.	Just like me.
I went up four flights of stairs.	Just like me.
I went into a little room.	Just like me.
I looked out a window.	Just like me.
I saw a monkey.	Just like me.

Just like you!

Will you remember me in fifty years?   Yes.
Will you remember me in twenty years?   Yes.
Will you remember me in ten years?   Yes.
Will you remember me in five years?   Yes.
Will you remember me next year?   Yes.
Will you remember me next month?   Yes.
Will you remember me next week?   Yes.
Will you remember me tomorrow?   Yes.
Will you remember me in another minute?   Yes.
Will you remember me in another second?   Yes.
Knock, knock.   Who's there?
See, you forgot me already.

113

Clowning

Making a clown face takes time and skill.

Every clown wears a different face.

A million tricks for a million laughs.
It's all in a day's work for a clown.

117

Think About It

1. Tell why you liked reading "Tell a Joke."
2. What are some of the things the clowns are doing in "Clowning Around"?
3. Why do clowns make you laugh?
4. Do you think clowns always feel like clowns? Why or why not?
5. If you were a clown, what would you do to make people laugh?

Create and Share

Cut out pictures of people laughing. Tell what you think is making each person laugh.

Explore

Choose a favorite joke from a book. Tell it to your friends.

Good Work, Amelia Bedelia

by Peggy Parish

"Amelia Bedelia," called Mr. Rogers.
"Is the coffee ready?"
"Coming right up," said Amelia Bedelia.
She poured a cup of coffee. She took it
into the dining room. "There," said Amelia
Bedelia. "Would you like something more?"

"Yes," said Mr. Rogers. "Toast and an egg."

"Fine," said Amelia Bedelia. She went into the kitchen. Very quickly Amelia Bedelia was back.

Mr. Rogers picked up the egg. He broke it over his toast. "Confound it, Amelia Bedelia!" he said. "I didn't say a raw egg!"

"But you didn't say to cook it," said Amelia Bedelia.

Mr. Rogers threw down his napkin. "Oh, go fly a kite," he said.

Amelia Bedelia looked surprised. "All
right," she said. "If you say so."

Soon Amelia Bedelia was out in a field.
She had a kite. "Now that was nice of Mr.
Rogers," she said. "I do love to fly kites,
but I better get back. Mrs. Rogers might
need me."

Sure enough, Mrs. Rogers was calling,
"Amelia Bedelia."

"Here I am," said Amelia Bedelia.

"There's a lot to do," said Mrs. Rogers. "Do you know how to make bread?"

"I make good corn bread," said Amelia Bedelia.

"No, I want white bread," said Mrs. Rogers. "You are a good cook. Just do what the recipe says."

"All right," said Amelia Bedelia.

"Here's a list of the other things I want you to do," said Mrs. Rogers. "I'll be out until dinner time."

"Don't worry," said Amelia Bedelia. "I'll get everything done."

Mrs. Rogers left.

"I'll start with that bread," said Amelia Bedelia. She read the recipe. "Do tell," she said, "I never knew bread did magic things."

Amelia Bedelia got everything she needed. Quickly she mixed the dough. Amelia Bedelia set the pan on the table. "Now," she said, "you're supposed to rise. This I've got to see."

Amelia Bedelia sat down to watch. But nothing happened. "Maybe you don't like to be watched. I'll come back," said Amelia Bedelia.

"Let's see." Amelia Bedelia got her list. "Clean out the ashes in the parlor fireplace. Fill the wood box." Amelia Bedelia went into the parlor. She cleaned out the ashes. Amelia Bedelia filled the wood box.

"That's done," said Amelia Bedelia. "What's next?" She read, "Pot the window box plants. Put the pots in the parlor."

Amelia Bedelia went outside. She counted the plants.

Then she went into the kitchen. "My goodness," she said. "I need every pot for this." So she took them all. Amelia Bedelia potted those plants, and she took them inside.

"Now I better tend to that bread," said
Amelia Bedelia. She went into the kitchen.
The bread still sat on the table. "Now look
here," she said. "You are supposed to rise.
Then I'm supposed to punch you down.
How can I punch if you don't rise?"

Amelia Bedelia sat down to think.
"Maybe the pan is too heavy," she said.
"I better help it rise."

Amelia Bedelia got some string. She
worked for a bit, and that bread began to
rise. "That should be high enough," said
Amelia Bedelia. "I'll just let you stay there
awhile."

Amelia Bedelia picked up her list. "Make a sponge cake." Amelia Bedelia read that again. "I know about a lot of cakes," she said, "and I never heard tell of that. But if she wants a sponge cake, I'll make her a sponge cake."

Amelia Bedelia put a little of this and some of that into a bowl. She mixed and mixed. "Now for the sponge," she said. Amelia Bedelia got a sponge. She snipped it into small pieces. "There," she said. "Into the cake you go." Soon the sponge cake was baking.

"I don't think Mr. Rogers will like this cake," said Amelia Bedelia. "I'll make my kind of cake too. He does love butterscotch icing."

So Amelia Bedelia baked another cake. "There now," she said. "I'll surprise him."

Amelia Bedelia put the butterscotch cake in the cupboard. She put the sponge cake on a shelf.

"My, this is a busy day," said Amelia
Bedelia. "Let's see what's next. Call
Alcolu. Ask him to patch the front door
screen." Amelia Bedelia shook her head.
"Alcolu can't patch anything," she said.
"I better do that myself." She got what she
needed. Then Amelia Bedelia patched
that screen.

Amelia Bedelia looked at the time. "Oh," she said. "I better get dinner started. Let me see what she wants."

She read the list. "A chicken dinner will be fine. What will she think of next?" Amelia said. "Well, that won't take long to fix."

Amelia Bedelia got everything ready. She set the table. Then she sat down to rest.

Soon Mr. and Mrs. Rogers came home. "Amelia Bedelia," yelled Mr. Rogers.

"Coming," called Amelia Bedelia.

"What is that awful cloth on the front door?" said Mrs. Rogers.

"You said to patch the screen," said Amelia Bedelia. "Can't patch without a patch."

They went into the parlor. "All my good pots!" said Mrs. Rogers.

"And bad ones too," said Amelia Bedelia.

Mr. Rogers looked at the wood box. He shook his head, but he didn't say a word.

They went into the kitchen. "The sponge cake is pretty," said Mrs. Rogers. "At least that's done right."

Something caught Mr. Rogers's eye. He looked up. "What in tarnation is that?" he said.

"The bread!" said Amelia Bedelia. "I plumb forgot it. Do let me punch it down quick." She climbed up on a chair. Amelia Bedelia began to punch.

Mr. and Mrs. Rogers just stared. The bread plopped to the floor.

"Did I see what I thought I saw?" said Mr. Rogers.

"You did," said Mrs. Rogers.

"Now," said Amelia Bedelia, "dinner is ready when you are."

"Well, you can cook," said Mrs. Rogers. "Dinner should be good."

"I hope so," said Mr. Rogers. "I'm hungry."

"Just serve the plates," said Mrs. Rogers.

Mr. and Mrs. Rogers sat at the table. Amelia Bedelia brought in the plates.

Mr. and Mrs. Rogers stared at the plates. "But, but, that's cracked corn. It's all kinds of awful things," said Mrs. Rogers.

"You said chicken dinner," said Amelia Bedelia. "That's what chickens eat for dinner."

Mrs. Rogers was too angry to speak.

"Take this mess away," said Mr. Rogers.

Mrs. Rogers said, "Serve the cake and coffee." Amelia Bedelia did.

Mr. Rogers took a big bite of cake. He spluttered and spit it out. "What in tarnation is in that?" he said.

"Sponge," said Amelia Bedelia. "Mrs. Rogers said to make a sponge cake."

Suddenly Mr. Rogers laughed. He roared.

Mrs. Rogers looked at the lumpy cake. Then she laughed too.

"But I'm still hungry," said Mr. Rogers.

"I can fix that," said Amelia Bedelia. "I have a surprise for you."

"Oh, no," said Mr. Rogers.

"I can't stand another one," said Mrs. Rogers.

Amelia Bedelia brought in milk and her butterscotch cake.

"Ahh," said Mr. Rogers.

"Hurry," said Mrs. Rogers.

Soon the whole cake was gone.

"How do you do it, Amelia Bedelia?" said Mr. Rogers. "One minute we're hopping mad at you."

"And the next, we know we can't do without you," said Mrs. Rogers.

Amelia Bedelia smiled. "I guess I just understand your ways," she said.

Did you know

▸ most sharks have at least 8 rows of teeth.

▸ a young chick has an "egg tooth" to help it break out of its shell.

▸ a crocodile has as many as 60 teeth but it does not chew.

Teeth Talk

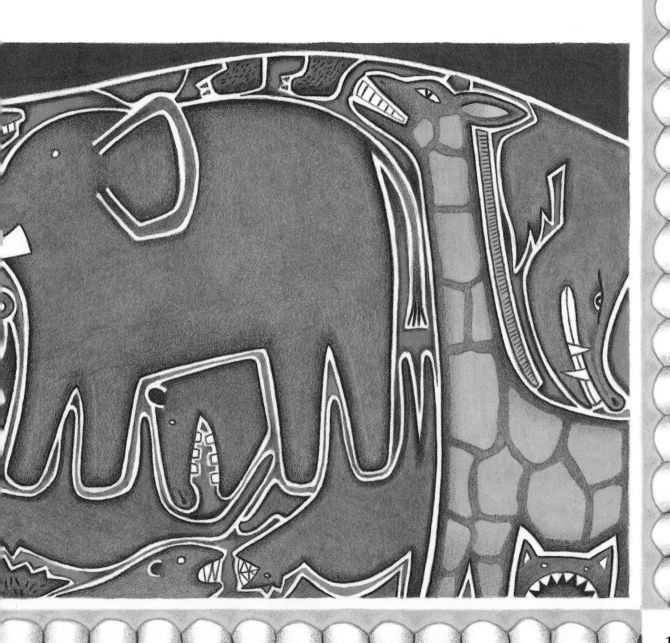

Heather's Feathers

by Leatie Weiss

Heather was the only bird in her class. She was the only one with feathers. She was the only one with a beak.

Everyone thought Heather was great. She could paint with her wings. She could win every race.

And then everything changed. It all began at snack time one morning.

Robbie was having a hard time eating his cookie. "It's because my front tooth is loose," he said. "I can't wait for it to fall out."

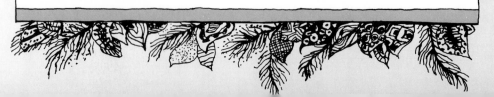

He wiggled it with his paw.

"I lost two teeth," said Patty.

"I lost four," said Amy. "How many did you lose, Heather?"

"None," said Heather. "You can't lose teeth if you don't have teeth."

"No teeth?" they all asked.

"My beak can do everything your teeth can do," said Heather.

"It can't get you a present from the Tooth Fairy," said Robbie. Then they all started laughing as if they knew a big secret.

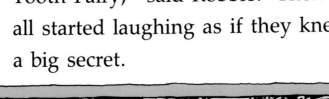

For the first time, Heather's feathers
drooped. She felt awful.

Suddenly Robbie began shouting, "My
tooth fell out!" What a fuss they all made.

"Put it under your pillow before you go
to sleep," said the teacher. "The Tooth
Fairy will leave you a present."

"So that's what the Tooth Fairy does,"
thought Heather. "What good is a beak?"

The next day Harold had lost a tooth.
Then Freddy's tooth was loose, too! All
they did was brag.

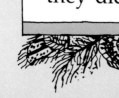

"I hate being a bird," thought Heather. "I don't even believe in the Tooth Fairy. If she was a real fairy, she'd help me grow a tooth!"

It was time for Show and Tell. Heather had brought her toy bear, but it was Harold's turn first. He had 50 cents to show from *you know who.*

"What did you bring today, Heather?" asked the teacher.

Heather hid her bear. "I forgot," she said, and started to cry.

The teacher tried to cheer her up. Then the bell rang. It was time to go home.

It was Father Bird's turn to drive home that day. He saw Heather's sad face.

"Cheer up," said Father. "I have a surprise for you. I baked a cake and you can help frost it."

"Who cares about cake?" cried Heather. "I want a surprise from the Tooth Fairy. I hate being a bird."

"Be proud you're a bird," said Father. "We know a few tricks, too."

"What kind of tricks?" asked Heather.

POP

"You'll see," said Father. "Maybe someday soon."

"I don't believe it," cried Heather. She gave her feathers a shake.

POP.

She shook, and feathers popped out! She flapped her wings. Out popped some more feathers. "I'm getting bald!" she screamed.

"You are not getting bald," said Father. "You are molting."

"Molting?" asked Heather. "What's molting?"

"It's your surprise trick. Your old feathers fall out. Then bright new ones grow in," said Father.

"I'm losing feathers," sang Heather. "That's even better than losing teeth!"

Heather began to dance. Her feathers went flying. She jumped into the pile. "What do I do with them?" she asked.

"Put them under your pillow," said Father.

"Will the Tooth Fairy come?" asked Heather.

"No," Father laughed. "But the Feather Fairy will."

That night, Heather thought of the feathers under her pillow. "Birds are so smart. Feathers are much softer to sleep on than teeth!"

The next day Heather got to school a bit late.

"I have something to show," she chirped. "I lost lots of feathers because I am growing up. And birds have a special fairy, too! Wait till you see the presents she left."

"Oooh! I wish I had feathers," said
Robbie.

"You can have some," said Heather. "I
got presents for everyone from the Feather
Fairy."

"Aren't we lucky to have Heather in our
class!" said the teacher.

"Oh, yes!" shouted everyone. "Heather's
feathers are better than the teeth we lost!"

Heather knew it was true. And she
popped out a few loose feathers to prove it.

Think About It

1. How is Heather different from everyone else in her class?
2. How does Heather feel about being different from her friends?
3. If the Feather Fairy were real, what presents might she give Heather?
4. How do you think Heather felt when she took her feathers to school?
5. Why does Heather change her mind about being different?

Create and Share

Write a thank-you note to the Feather Fairy from Heather.

Explore

Look for books about birds. Find out some ways birds use their feathers. Make a list.

Animal Teeth

by Meg Buckley

The next time you see a dog yawn, take a look inside its mouth. You will see some very sharp teeth. This is because a dog eats meat and needs sharp teeth to chew.

There are many different kinds of animal teeth. Some animals need teeth for eating meat. Others need teeth for eating plants. Some use their teeth to fight off other animals. Others use their teeth as tools.

Dogs and cats have sharp teeth because they eat meat. Wolves and lions have sharp teeth too. Wolves and lions must catch other animals for food. They would not be able to do this if their teeth were dull.

150

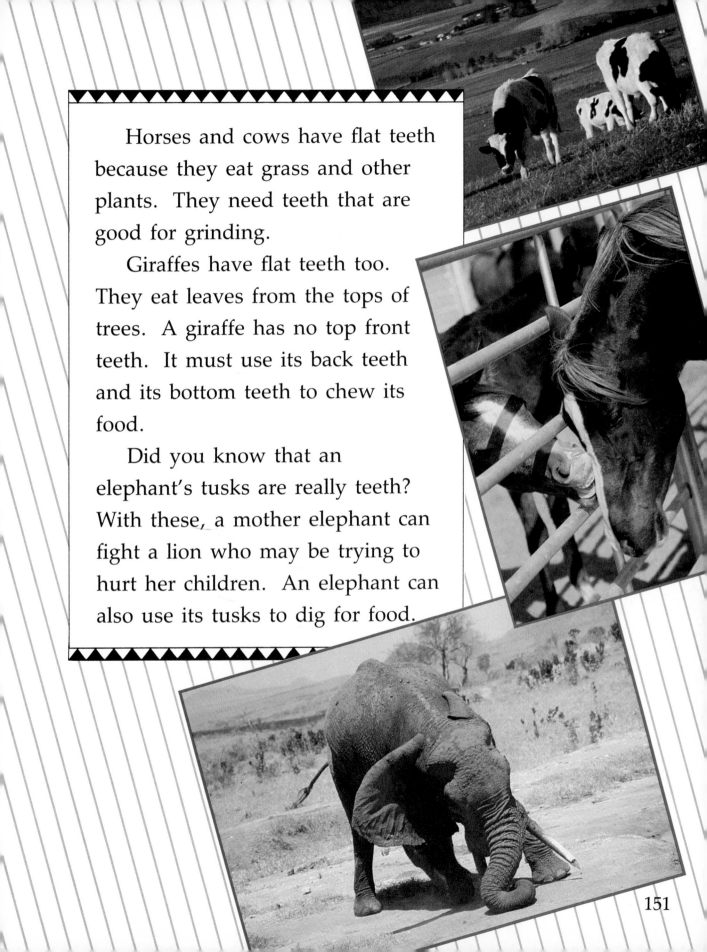

Horses and cows have flat teeth because they eat grass and other plants. They need teeth that are good for grinding.

Giraffes have flat teeth too. They eat leaves from the tops of trees. A giraffe has no top front teeth. It must use its back teeth and its bottom teeth to chew its food.

Did you know that an elephant's tusks are really teeth? With these, a mother elephant can fight a lion who may be trying to hurt her children. An elephant can also use its tusks to dig for food.

Beavers have four large front teeth. With these a beaver can chop down trees to make its home on a pond.

A walrus needs help getting onto an iceberg. It uses its long tusks to pull itself out of the water. A walrus can also use its tusks to fight off polar bears.

Teeth are very important to animals. Teeth help them do many things. That is why animals have the kinds of teeth they do.

Think About It

1. List some ways animals use their teeth.
2. Why do horses and cows have different teeth from cats and dogs?
3. What kind of teeth do you think people have?
4. If you found an animal skull, how could you tell if the animal ate meat or plants?

Create and Share

Find a picture of an animal using its teeth. Write about what it is doing.

Explore

Find out about the teeth of rabbits, bears, or squirrels.

Molly
and the
by Pat Ross
Slow Teeth

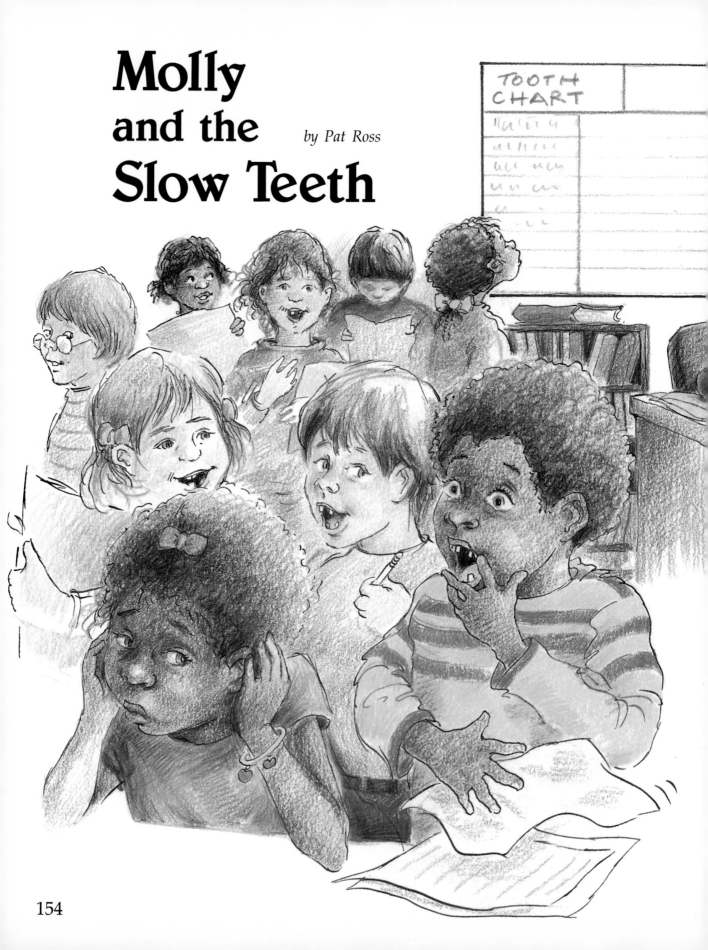

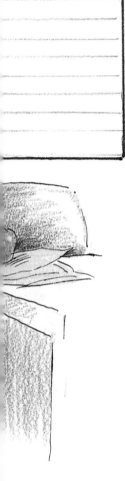

Molly Davis had not lost one tooth yet. And she was already in second grade. She checked her teeth for loose ones every day. She tried to wiggle the big top teeth.

Not a budge! She tried to push the little bottom teeth. Stuck tight!

"You've just got slow teeth," her mother said. "They'll come out when they're ready."

Everybody else in her class had spaces where teeth used to be. Everybody else had their name on the Tooth Chart in the front of the room. Only Molly's name was missing.

Marvin Wilson had the fastest teeth in the class. His name was on the Tooth Chart eight times. He already had five grown-up teeth.

He counted them every day. "One, two . . ." Marvin would begin to count.

He pointed and counted out loud. Molly covered her ears before he got to "five."

Susan was Molly's best friend. Susan
had a special tooth pillow with a little
pocket on top that said "My Tooth." One
day, Susan held it up for Molly to see.

"That makes *four!*" said Molly when she
saw another tooth.

"We can share the pillow," said Susan.

It was hard for Molly to share a pillow
that had somebody else's tooth inside.

That night, Molly had a plan to fool the
Tooth Fairy.

She put a stone under her pillow. It
was small and white, and shaped just like
a tooth.

"I hope the Tooth Fairy checks tonight," Molly called to her mother.

"Don't worry," her mother said. "The Tooth Fairy works very late, so sweet dreams."

The next morning, Molly found a dime under her pillow. There was also a note.

At school, Molly tried to keep her mind off her teeth. But even the lunch milk made her think of strong teeth.

Molly played with her front teeth during math class. After class, Marvin told Molly about a way to pull teeth. You only needed a string and a doorknob. She had lots of both at home.

Before dinner, Molly picked a big top tooth. She tied one end of the string to her tooth. She tied the other end to a doorknob. Marvin said all you had to do was slam the door hard. *Zip*—the tooth would pop out. But Marvin did not say if it hurt.

Just then, Molly's father walked by. "Looks like somebody tied you up," he said.

"No jokes today," said Molly.

"Hurting your mouth is no joke," her father said.

"That's just what I was thinking," said Molly.

Together they took the string off the tooth and the doorknob.

At bedtime, her top tooth felt very sore. She asked her mother to test it.

"I can't tell," said her mother. "Maybe it's sore from so much testing."

"I'll never lose a tooth!" cried Molly. "I'll be a grown-up with baby teeth! I'm never checking my dumb, tight, slow teeth again—ever!"

Molly cried hard into her pillow until at last she fell asleep.

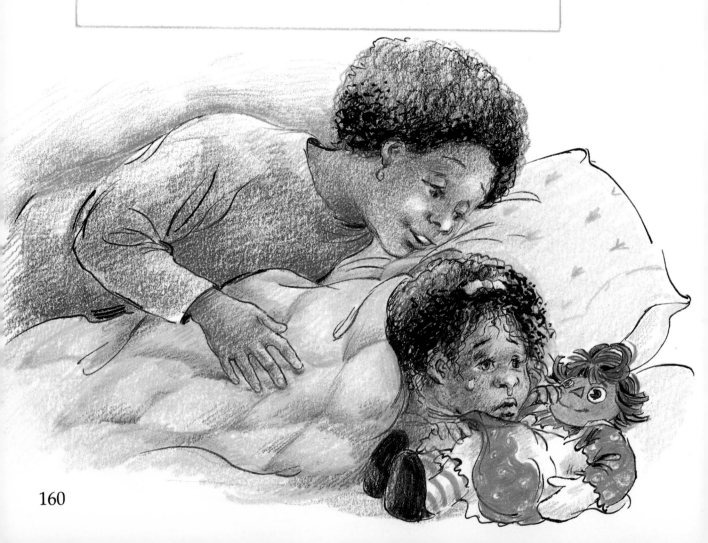

Molly did not check her teeth for almost a week. That was the week they learned all about dinosaurs.

Then one day, Marvin asked about dinosaur teeth. That made Molly think about her own teeth. She pushed the bottom teeth with her tongue. They were still stuck. Then she tried the top teeth. One wiggled! Molly had a loose tooth. She couldn't believe it!

Molly's tooth got looser and looser. It wiggled and it wobbled. Then it bent all the way back. Molly could even twist it around. But still that tooth *would not* come out.

Day after day, all her friends helped test the tooth. Day after day, Molly and her friends waited.

One day at lunch, everybody was acting silly. Susan said, "Have some dinosaur, my dear!"

Everybody laughed.

Then Molly acted like she was a hungry dinosaur. She roared and she snorted. Then she took a big bite of her apple. Everybody really laughed at that!

Molly stopped acting silly. "Who put rocks in my apple?" she asked.

Everybody stopped roaring and snorting. Molly reached into her mouth and pulled out something small and white.

"Your tooth!" cried Susan.

"*Some* rock," said Marvin.

163

Dear Molly,
Even slow teeth come out when they are ready. You keep this one. There will be lots more for me.
Love,
Your own
Tooth Fairy

Molly stuck her tongue through the space where the tooth used to be. It felt soft and bare.

"Well," said Molly to her tooth, "you sure took your time."

The next morning, the tooth was still under her pillow. Next to it were a quarter and a note.

Molly dressed fast. She didn't want to be late for school. Tooth Chart time came first. And Molly knew that a place on the Tooth Chart was waiting just for her.

Think About It

1. Why did Molly want to lose a tooth?
2. How did Molly feel when her teeth did not get loose?
3. How is Molly like Heather in "Heather's Feathers"?
4. Have you ever felt the way Molly did? Tell about it.

Create and Share

Write about a time you lost a tooth.

Explore

Find out about how to care for your teeth.
Talk to a dentist or read a book.

A friend in need is a friend indeed.

A Big Help

The Lion and the Mouse

Aesop fable retold by Anne Terry White

In the heat of the day a lion lay asleep by the woods. He lay so still that a mouse ran right across his nose without knowing it was a nose.

Bang! The lion clapped his paw to his face. He had caught something. It was furry. Lazily he opened his eyes. He lifted up one side of his huge paw just a little bit to see what was under it. He smiled when he saw a mouse.

"Let me go, Great King!" he heard the little mouse squeak in her tiny voice. "I didn't mean to do it! Let me go, and someday I will repay you."

"That's very funny," said the lion, and he laughed. "How can a little thing like you help me, the great King of Beasts?"

"I don't know," the mouse said, "but a little animal *can* sometimes help a big one."

"Well, you have made me laugh," the lion said, "and I don't laugh very often. Anyway, you would hardly make half a meal for me." He lifted his paw and let the mouse go.

A few days later the lion was caught in a net. The woods rang with his angry roaring and the little mouse heard him.

"That is my kind lion!" she cried. "He is in trouble!" As fast as she could, she ran toward the spot where the lion was. The lion was thrashing around so in the net that the mouse didn't dare to come near for fear of being crushed.

"O King, be still!" she cried. "I will chew through the ropes and set you free."

So the lion lay still while the mouse worked away with her sharp teeth. And in a short time the lion was able to creep out of the net.

"You see? I told you I would repay you," the mouse said happily. "A little animal sometimes really can help a big one."

The lion smiled because he knew it was true.

Little friends are often great friends.

Think About It

1. Why did the lion let the mouse go?
2. How did the lion feel about the mouse's promise?
3. What do you think the lion learned?
4. How does the story show that by helping others you can often help yourself?

Create and Share

Tell about a time you helped someone older or bigger.

Explore

Read other Aesop fables.

Animal Helpers

by Kathleen S. Coleman

Every day there are people around you who help animals stay happy and healthy. These people are animal helpers. There are many kinds of animal helpers.

Where would you take your pet if it was sick? You would go to a veterinarian. People call this kind of doctor a vet. The vet will try to help your pet get better.

She will check your pet's ears and eyes the same way a doctor would check yours. The vet will also listen to your pet's heart. Sometimes a vet will also take an X ray or give your pet a shot.

There are other animal helpers too. A zookeeper is someone who takes care of the animals in the zoo. He feeds the animals every day. A zookeeper also cleans their cages. It is the zookeeper's job to make sure the animals are happy and healthy.

There are animal helpers in the forest. They are called forest rangers. They help animals such as rabbits, foxes, and bears. Forest rangers watch for forest fires. Forest fires burn the food that animals eat. Fires also burn down animal homes. If a fire starts, the ranger will let fire fighters know. They can put out a fire before it hurts the forest and the animals that live there.

There are also people who help the animals in the ocean. They help animals such as whales, sharks, and seals. Sometimes these people work in the ocean. Sometimes these people work on land. Their job is to see if the water is clean enough for the animals to live in. They also see if there is enough food for the animals to eat.

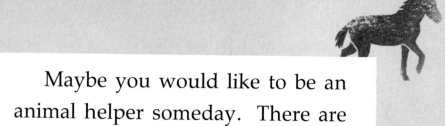

Maybe you would like to be an animal helper someday. There are a few things you can do right now to help animals. Make sure you take good care of your pet. Follow the rules at the zoo. When you go to a forest, don't play with matches. Don't litter at the beach because the water is home to many animals. If you remember these things, you will be an animal helper too.

178

Think About It

1. Make a list of some things animal helpers do.
2. In what ways are the jobs of a zookeeper and a forest ranger different?
3. What are some problems animals in the ocean may have?
4. What can *you* do to help animals?
5. Tell about a time you helped an animal.

Create and Share

List some ways animals can help people.

Explore

Find out more about one of the animal helpers in this story.

Señor Billy Goat

by Pura Belpré

There once was a little old woman and a little old man living in Puerto Rico. They were very happy living in their straw hut. Together they shared a vegetable garden.

In the morning while his wife was busy, the husband would rush to the window, and say, "Oh, María! Look at my beautiful lettuce. There is nothing in the garden like it."

That would bring María running to the window, and she would say, "Oh, Ramón! Put on your glasses and see for yourself. You must be as blind as a bat. Look at my corn. It is good enough for a king."

And then both would laugh at each other and turn back to eat their breakfast.

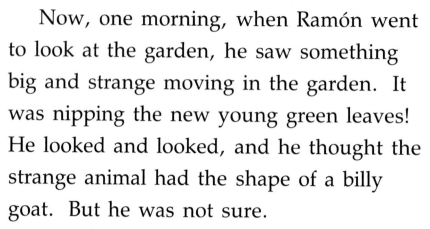

Now, one morning, when Ramón went to look at the garden, he saw something big and strange moving in the garden. It was nipping the new young green leaves! He looked and looked, and he thought the strange animal had the shape of a billy goat. But he was not sure.

"María! María!" he called. "Come here quick. Something big and strange is eating up our garden. Look," he said. "Do you see what I see?"

"Oh, Ramón," said María. "A billy goat came to eat our garden. What shall we do?"

"Do not worry," said Ramón. "I will make him go away."

Ramón went down to the field. He patted the billy goat on its back and said, "Hello, Señor Billy Goat. Please do not eat up the garden. Please go away."

But Señor Billy Goat turned and went at
Ramón with his horns all set.

"Oh, María! María!" cried the old man,
running up the hill as fast as he could.
"Open the door, please! The billy goat is
after me." Puffing and panting, poor
Ramón dropped on a chair and began to cry.

"Do not cry," said María. "I will go to
the billy goat and make him go away."
She went down to the field.

She went to where the billy goat was. She said, "Hello, Señor Billy Goat. That is a fine breakfast you are having. I wonder if you know how long it takes to plant the seeds and pull the weeds. However, I came to ask you . . ."

That was as far as she got because the billy goat turned and headed toward her.

The little old woman ran up the hill, yelling, "Oh, Ramón! The billy goat is after me. Open the door, please!" And she, too, ran inside the hut.

"Oh my," she cried.

"No more lettuce and corn," cried the old man.

They cried and cried. Then suddenly something stung Ramón's ear. He shook his head to get rid of it. As he did, a little black ant dropped right into his hand.

"María, look!" he cried.

"I have come to help you," the ant whispered. "What will you give me if I do so?"

"How can you help us, little ant?" asked María.

"You are so small. What can you do?" asked Ramón.

"I can make Señor Billy Goat go away," said the ant.

"You!" cried María.

"Yes, what will you give me if I do so?"

"Anything you want," said Ramón.

"Yes, yes, anything," said María.

The ant thought for a while. Then she asked for a little sack of flour and one of sugar for her family.

187

Ramón and María promised, and the little black ant crawled down. She went through a crack in the floor. Out into the open she crawled until she reached the field. There was the billy goat. He was still eating in the garden. The ant crawled up the goat's leg and up his back. She went into the goat's ear and stung him.

"Ouch!" cried the billy goat, and he raised one leg to scratch himself. But the little ant had now moved to the other ear. She stung him again with all her might.

"Ouch!" cried the billy goat again, and he raised his other leg to scratch his other ear. But by that time the little ant was going up and down his back, stinging the goat.

"Ouch! Ouch! An ant hill! I have stepped on an ant hill," the billy goat cried.

He jumped out of the vegetable patch.
Thinking that he was all covered with ants,
the goat rolled on the ground to shake
them off. He rolled and rolled. Faster and
faster he went—rolling . . . rolling . . .
rolling . . . He forgot he was on a hill,
and so he found himself going down,
down the hill and out of sight. For all I
know, he is still rolling.

But Ramón and María gave the little ant
one little sack of flour and one little sack
of sugar. Since then they have lived
happily in their hut.

Think About It

1. Why are María and Ramón so upset about the goat in their garden?
2. How did they try to get rid of the goat?
3. What did María and Ramón learn?
4. Did you ever try to get someone to stop doing something you didn't like by talking to him or her? Did it work?
5. Tell how the mouse in "The Lion and the Mouse" and the ant in "Señor Billy Goat" are the same.

Create and Share

Make cutouts of the people and animals in the story. Tell the story with your cutouts.

Explore

Find out how real ants help farmers.

What's Ticking?

It's hands are always on its face.
When it goes, it stays in one place.

What is it? *(A clock)*

Clocks and More Clocks

by Pat Hutchins

One day Mr. Higgins found a clock in the attic. It looked very splendid standing there.

"How do I know if it's correct?" he thought. So he went out and bought another which he placed in the bedroom.

"Three o'clock," said Mr. Higgins. "I'll see if the other clock is right." He ran up to the attic, but the clock said one minute past three.

"How do I know which one is right?" he thought. So he went out and bought another, which he placed in the kitchen.

"Ten minutes to four. I'll check the others." He ran up to the attic. The attic clock said eight minutes to four. He ran down to the bedroom. The bedroom clock said seven minutes to four.

"I still don't know which
one is right," he thought.
So he went out and bought
another, which he placed
in the hall.

"Twenty minutes past four," he said,
and ran up to the attic. The attic clock said
twenty-three minutes past four. He ran
down to the kitchen. The kitchen clock
said twenty-five minutes past four. He ran
up to the bedroom. The bedroom clock
said twenty-six minutes past four.

"This is no good at all," thought Mr.
Higgins. And he went to the Clockmaker.
"My hall clock says twenty minutes past
four, my attic clock says twenty-three
minutes past four, my kitchen clock says
twenty-five minutes past four, my bedroom
clock says twenty-six minutes past four,
and I don't know which one is right!" said
Mr. Higgins.

So the Clockmaker went to the house to look at the clocks. The hall clock said five o'clock.

"There's nothing wrong with this clock," said the Clockmaker. "Look!"

The kitchen clock said one minute past five. "There!" shouted Mr. Higgins. "Your watch said five o'clock."

"But it is one minute past now!" said the Clockmaker. "Look!"

The attic clock said three minutes past five.

"There's nothing wrong with this clock either," said the Clockmaker. "Look!"

"What a wonderful watch!" said Mr. Higgins. And he went out and bought one. And ever since he bought his watch, all his clocks have been right.

Think About It

1. Why did Mr. Higgins keep getting more clocks?
2. What was so silly about the way Mr. Higgins acted?
3. How did the Clockmaker help Mr. Higgins with his problem?
4. What do you think the Clockmaker thought of Mr. Higgins?
5. Tell Mr. Higgins why each clock had a different time.

Create and Share

Cut out pictures of many clocks. Use them to make a big picture of clocks.

Explore

Ask five people where they keep clocks in their houses. Find out why people like to put clocks in these rooms.

Old Ways of Telling Time

from TIME by Feenie Ziner and Elizabeth Thompson

morning

noon

night

How do you
know what time it is?
You can tell something about
time by looking at the sun. It is
morning at sunrise. It is noon when the
sun is highest in the sky. It is night when
the sun sets.

When the sun shines on the other side
of our planet Earth, it is night for us.

You cannot count hours just by looking
at the sun. But long before the clocks
of today, people did find
ways to keep track
of time.

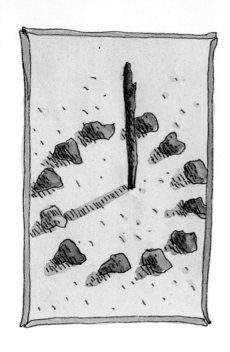

Shadow Sticks

A shadow stick can help us count the hours. A shadow stick points straight up. The stones around the stick mark the hours.

A shadow stick is like a clock. As the earth turns, the sun makes the shadow of the stick fall on the stones. The shadow moves from one stone to the next in one hour.

Can you tell time on a cloudy day with a shadow stick?

No.

Can you tell time at night with a shadow stick?

No.

Sundials

A sundial is like a shadow stick. It can only tell time when the sun is shining.

Candle Clocks

There is a way to tell time that works both night and day. It works when it is sunny or cloudy. It is a candle clock.

A candle clock is painted with bands of color. It takes an hour for each band to burn. If you light a candle clock at 8 o'clock and burn 2 bands, what time will it be?

Ten o'clock.

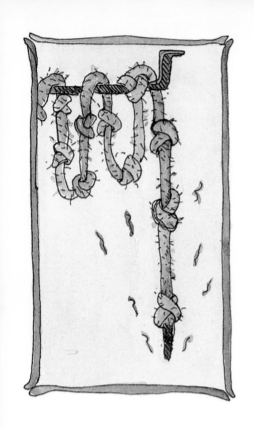

Rope Clocks

People can count hours by burning ropes. They tie knots in the rope to mark the hours. It takes one hour for the rope to burn from one knot to the next.

Candle clocks and rope clocks do not need the sun.

Can the candle clock or the rope clock be used over again? No.

Water Clocks

Water clocks were used long, long ago. The first water clock measured the water leaking out of a big pot. Different water lines were marked on the pot—one for each hour. People could tell time by looking at the line and the water left in the pot.

Water clocks did not need the sun. They could work at night. They could be used over and over again.

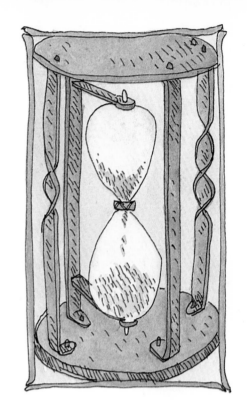

Hourglass

Another way of telling time is with an hourglass. It has an odd shape. Sand falls from the top to the bottom. This takes one hour. Then the glass is turned upside down. An hourglass also can be used again and again.

Can you think of some problems people may have had using water clocks and hourglasses? What are they?

These old ways of telling time were not as good as today's clocks. But they did help count the hours.

Tick
Tock Clock

Tick tock,
tick tock,
something's hiding
in the clock,
a thing that makes
a ticking sound
and helps the hands
go round and round,
a thing that can't
be very tall
to fit inside
a place that small.
Tick tock,
tick tock,
something's hiding
in the clock.

—Jack Prelutsky

Think About It

1. List the different clocks that you learned about in "Old Ways of Telling Time."
2. Next to each clock you listed above, tell what problem it had.
3. How are clocks of today better than the old ways of telling time?
4. Tell what you think is hiding in the clock from "Tick Tock Clock."

Create and Share

List some times when "time goes too fast" and "time goes too slow." Share your list with others.

Explore

Some clocks use Roman numerals. Find out how to write the Roman numerals, 1–12.

The dinosaurs are all gone. Where can you
   see-em?
In the museum.

THE ONLY PLACE
by William Cole

Dinosaurs

Dinosaur Facts

by Hal Ober

Dinosaurs are fun and a little scary to imagine. Some of them were very big. Now only giant bones and footprints are left to tell their story. No wonder people keep talking about them.

Many millions of years ago the world did not look like it does today. The earth had one giant land that was warm and wet. Thick jungles of plants grew everywhere. Many of the animals that walked the land had bodies low to the ground and legs on the sides of their bodies.

As time passed, the land changed. The animals changed too. Some of the animals now had legs under their bodies. They moved faster than the other animals. These new animals were the first dinosaurs, or "terrible lizards."

213

Dinosaurs came in all sizes. One of the biggest was a Brachiosaurus. It was about 75 feet long. That is longer than three school buses.

It was so tall it could have peeked through the top window of a four-story building. It weighed as much as ten elephants. The Brachiosaurus ate the leaves on the tops of tall trees. Imagine how many leaves a Brachiosaurus had to eat!

Not all dinosaurs grew as big as the Brachiosaurus. The Stegosaurus was only as long as one bus. It weighed less than a hippopotamus. It just wanted to be left alone to chew on soft leaves with its short teeth. Along its back was a row of pointed plates. On the end of its tail were four long spikes. Even though its brain was no bigger than a walnut, a Stegosaurus knew how to fight back.

216

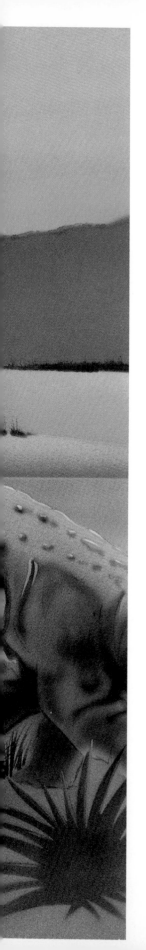

The Triceratops was about as long as a bus too. It looked like a giant rhinoceros. It had three long horns. One horn was on its nose. The Triceratops also had sharp teeth that were good for chewing the tough leaves of the palm tree.

The most terrible of the terrible lizards may have been the Tyrannosaurus. It ate other dinosaurs. It walked on its hind legs and was about 50 feet long. Its teeth and claws were as long as knives. Only its arms looked small. Its arms may have helped the Tyrannosaurus push itself up off the ground.

The Tyrannosaurus was one of the last dinosaurs. The dinosaurs all died about 65 million years ago. Some people think that it got too cold for the dinosaurs. Other people think the dinosaurs couldn't find enough food to eat. No one is sure why the dinosaurs all died but lots of people are still making guesses about it.

Dinosaur Sizes

	How long?	How tall?	How heavy?
Brachiosaurus	75 feet	40 feet	75 tons
Stegosaurus	30 feet	10 feet	2 tons
Triceratops	30 feet	8 feet	8 tons
Tyrannosaurus	50 feet	20 feet	7 tons

Think About It

1. How do people find out about dinosaurs?
2. List the dinosaurs in the story from smallest to biggest.
3. What animals that live today look almost like dinosaurs?
4. Which dinosaur frightened most other dinosaurs?
5. Why do you think the dinosaurs died?

Create and Share

Write about your favorite dinosaur. Draw a picture showing how it looked.

Explore

Add other dinosaurs to the chart on page 218. Look for books that will tell you their sizes.

Dinosaurs at Home

by Jan Hurwitz

Now that you know some facts
about dinosaurs, you might want to
make your own dinosaur and dinosaur
home. The steps that follow
will show you how.

For the dinosaur, you will need:

paper
scissors
pencil
crayons
paste
tape
a straw

For the dinosaur's home, you will need:

shoe box
small stones
tree twig
finger bandage

Making the dinosaur

1. Trace the dinosaur on page 222 onto your paper. Be sure to trace the dotted lines onto your paper also.

2. Fold the dinosaur in half on the dotted lines.

3. Cut out the folded dinosaur. (*Do not cut where you have the dotted lines.*)

222

4. Color your dinosaur.

5. Paste both sides of the head together.

6. Cut the straw into four pieces. Each piece should be two inches long.

7. Tape a piece of the straw on the inside of each foot. This will make the dinosaur stand up better.

Making the dinosaur's home

1. Cut out one long side of the shoe box.

2. Color in the sky, sun, grass, flowers, and mountains, to make your dinosaur's home.

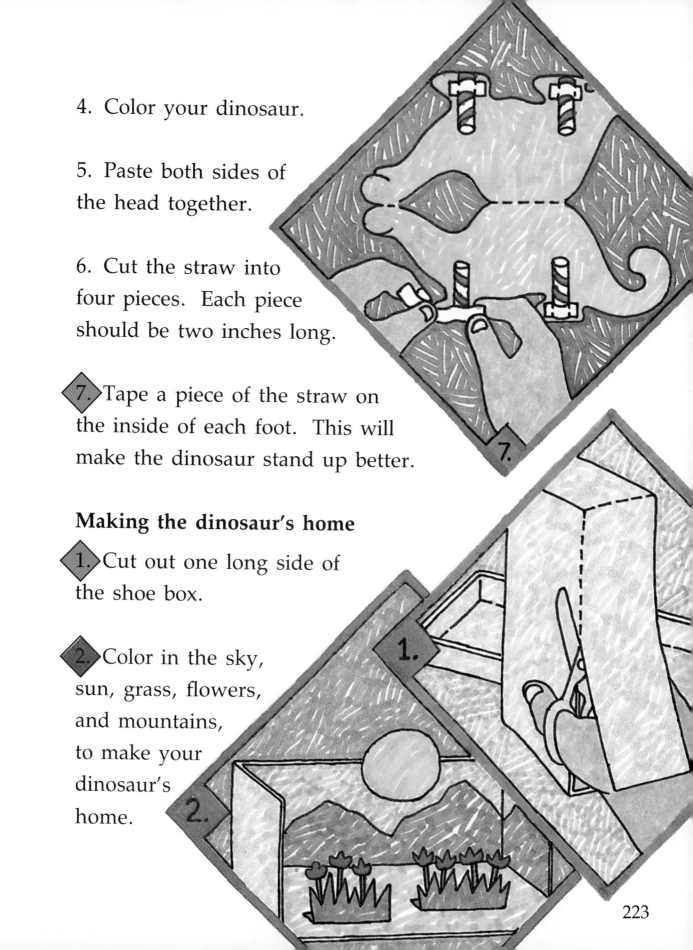

3. Use the bandage to make the little twigs stick to the back of your biggest stone. Put the bandage on real tight and press the sticky parts firmly onto the stone. Now your tree can stand in a corner of the box. Put the other stones around the tree.

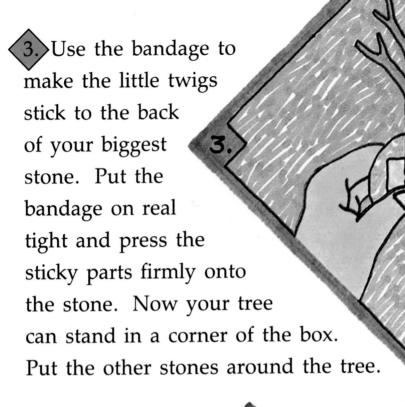

Now put your dinosaur in its new home!

Think About It

1. What things do you need to make the dinosaur and its home?
2. Tell two ways to make your dinosaur stand.
3. How can you find out what color to make your dinosaur?
4. What do you think a real dinosaur would like in its home?

Create and Share

Write about a place a real dinosaur would *not* like to live. Tell why.

Explore

Find out about other ways to make dinosaurs or other animals.

Nate the Great and the Sticky Case

by Marjorie Weinman Sharmat

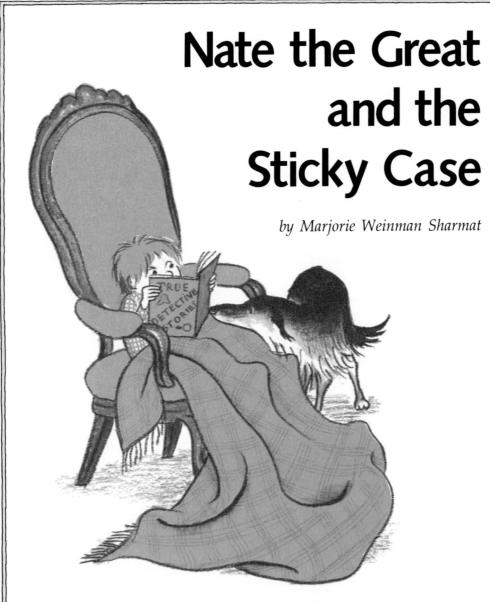

I, Nate the Great, was drying off from the rain. I was sitting under a blanket and reading a detective book. My dog Sludge was sniffing it. I was on Page 33 when I heard a knock. I opened the door. Claude was there.

"I lost my best dinosaur," Claude said.

He was always losing things.

"This is your biggest loss yet," I said.
"A dinosaur is huge. How could you lose it?"

"My dinosaur is small," Claude said.
"It is a Stegosaurus on a stamp. Can you
help me find it?"

"It is hard to find something that
small," I said. "This will be a big case.
But I will take it. Tell me, where was the
Stegosaurus stamp the last time you saw it?"

"It was on a table in my house," Claude said. "I was showing all my dinosaur stamps to my friends. The Stegosaurus stamp was my favorite."

"Who are your friends?" I asked.

"Annie, Pip, Rosamond, and you. But you weren't there," Claude added.

"Good thinking," I said. "I, Nate the Great, will go to your house and look at your table." I wrote a note to my mother.

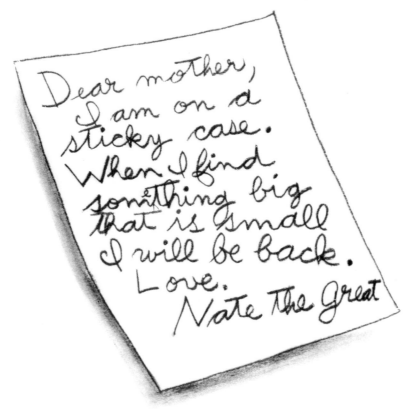

Dear mother,
I am on a sticky case. When I find something big that is small I will be back.
Love,
Nate The Great

Claude and I went to his house. He showed me his table. It had stamps all over it.

"Here are all of my stamps," Claude said. "Except for the Stegosaurus stamp."

I, Nate the Great, saw a Tyrannosaurus stamp. I saw a Brontosaurus stamp. I did not see a Stegosaurus stamp.

"Where was the Stegosaurus stamp when it was on the table?" I asked.

"Near the edge," Claude said.

"It must have fallen off," I said. I looked on the floor near the table. The Stegosaurus stamp was not there. I picked up a stamp and showed it to Sludge.

"We must look for a lost stamp," I said.

Sometimes Sludge is not a great detective. He tried to lick the sticky side of the stamp.

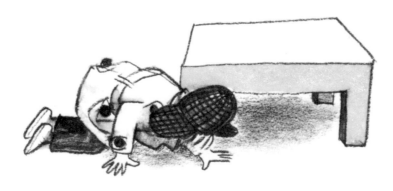

"*Look*. Don't lick," I said.

Sludge and I looked at, over, under, and around everything in Claude's house. Then we looked again. We did not find the Stegosaurus stamp.

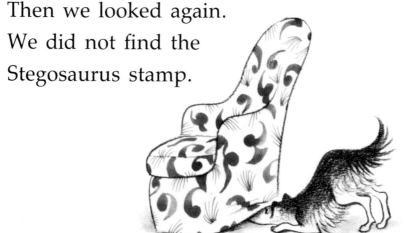

"The Stegosaurus stamp is not in your house," I said. "Tell me, when did you notice the stamp was missing?"

"After everybody left," Claude said.

"Did everybody leave together?" I asked.

"Yes," said Claude.

"Did everybody come together?" I asked.

"No," said Claude. "Annie and
Rosamond came to tell me that Rosamond
was going to have a yard sale. Then it
started to rain. It rained for a long time.
So Annie and Rosamond stayed and looked
at my stamps. When the rain stopped, Pip
came over. He looked at my stamps, too.
Then they all left together to go to
Rosamond's yard sale."

"Then I, Nate the Great, must go to the
yard sale, too," I said. "I must speak to
everyone who was in the room with the
Stegosaurus stamp."

Sludge and I went to Rosamond's
house. Rosamond was standing in her
yard with her four cats under a sign.

"Are you selling your cats?" I asked.

"No," Rosamond said. "I am selling
and swapping empty tuna fish cans, slippers,
spare cat hairs, toothbrushes, pictures of
milk, spoons, and all sorts of things."

"Do you have a Stegosaurus stamp?"
I asked.

"No," Rosamond said. "But I saw one
at Claude's house, near the edge of his
table."

I saw Pip looking at some empty tuna fish cans. "Did you see a Stegosaurus stamp at the edge of Claude's table?" I asked.

Pip doesn't say much. He shook his head up and down.

"Do you know where it is now?" I asked.

Pip shook his head sideways.

"Thank you," I said.

I saw Annie and her dog Fang.

"I am looking for Claude's Stegosaurus stamp," I said. "What do you know about it?"

"I know that the Stegosaurus is pretty," Annie said. "I know that it looks like Fang." Annie turned toward Fang. "Show us your Stegosaurus smile," she said.

Fang opened his mouth. I, Nate the Great, knew it was time to go home. I said good-by to Annie. Sludge and I walked home slowly.

At home I made some pancakes. I gave Sludge a bone. We ate and thought. Where was the Stegosaurus stamp? This was a sticky case. I, Nate the Great, was stuck.

I thought hard. What did I know about the Stegosaurus stamp? I knew that Annie and Rosamond went to Claude's house and saw the stamp. Then it rained for a long time. I knew that after the rain stopped, Pip went to Claude's house and saw the stamp, too. I knew the stamp had been at the edge of Claude's table. I knew it was not in Claude's house now.

Perhaps I had been thinking wrong. Perhaps I had forgotten that there are two sides to every stamp. Perhaps I should think about the sticky side.

"Think sticky," I said to Sludge. Sludge was licking his dog bowl. He had not been much help on this case. Or had he?

I remembered when Sludge tried to lick the sticky side of the stamp. Sludge's wet tongue would have made the stamp very sticky. A very sticky stamp . . . sticks!

Suddenly I knew that Sludge was a great detective. He knew that the sticky side of the stamp could be important. I, Nate the Great, knew that anything wet would make a stamp very sticky.

I thought of wet things. I thought of rain. When Annie and Rosamond went to Claude's house it was not raining. But when Pip went to Claude's house it had been raining and stopped. I, Nate the Great, thought of puddles. I thought of Pip stepping in them.

I got a stamp from my desk and put it on the floor. I went outside and stepped in a few puddles. Then I went back inside and stepped on the sticky side of the stamp. The stamp stuck to my shoe! The same thing must have happened to the Stegosaurus stamp and Pip's shoe at Claude's house. Now I knew that I had to see Pip's shoes.

Sludge and I went to Pip's house. I rang the bell. Pip opened the door. He was wearing slippers.

"Where are your shoes?" I asked.

Pip looked down at his feet. Then he said, "My shoes were all wet from the rain. After I left Claude's house I swapped them for a pair of dry slippers at Rosamond's yard sale. I took the slippers off the Swap Table and put my shoes there."

"Thank you," I said.

Sludge and I went back to Rosamond's yard sale. We went up to the Swap Table.

"The sticky case is almost over," I said. "I want Pip's shoes. Where are they?"

"I just sold them to Annie for ten
cents," Rosamond said. "It was my big
sale of the day."

Sludge and I ran to Annie's house. She
was outside with Fang. I saw two shoes.
One was on the ground. The other was in
Fang's mouth.

"Are these Pip's shoes?" I asked.

"They were," Annie said. "I bought
them for Fang to chew."

I, Nate the Great, saw the bottom of the
shoe Fang was chewing. Something small,
square, and dirty was stuck to it. At last I
had found the Stegosaurus stamp.

But I, Nate the Great, knew that finding was not everything. Getting was important, too. I thought fast.

"Show me Fang's Stegosaurus smile," I said.

"Smile, Fang," Annie said.

Fang smiled. The shoe fell to the ground. I picked it up. I, Nate the Great, peeled off the stamp. The case was solved. We took the Stegosaurus stamp to Claude's house. The stamp was dirty, sticky, icky, and ugly. But Claude was happy to get it.

Sludge and I walked home. We were careful not to step in any puddles.

Glossary

A

above in a higher place
(The stars were shining *above*.)

already by this time (By ten
o'clock, you should *already* be
at school.)

angry mad; feeling anger
(Molly was *angry* when she
couldn't find her crayons.)
angrier, angriest

around on all sides of (In a
toy shop, there are many
toys *around* you.)

attic a room at the top of some
houses, just under the roof
(My family puts the things
we don't use in the *attic*.)

B

backwards with the back end
first (The car moved
backwards down the road.)

bandage a strip of cloth or
paper that you put over a
place on your body that has
been hurt (When I cut my
finger, Mom puts a *bandage*
on it.)

beautiful very pretty (My
new dress is *beautiful*.)

beaver an animal with brown
fur and a wide tail that lives
on land and in the water
(The *beaver* cut down a tree
with its teeth.)

because for a reason (I am
afraid *because* it is dark here.)

began See **begin.**

begin   to start (Please read the story that *begins* on page 100.) **began, begun, beginning**

believe   to think something is true (I do not *believe* the story that Billy told.) **believed, believing**

big   great in size; large (That hill is *big*, but a mountain is much *bigger*.) **bigger, biggest**

blind   not able to see (Ben helped the *blind* man find his hat.)

bottom   the lowest part (Mr. Ling saw a fish swimming near the *bottom* of the river.)

bought   See **buy**.

burglar   someone who goes into a house to steal things (Jenny put a lock on the door to keep out *burglars*.)

busy   having a lot to do (The bees were very *busy* making honey.) **busier, busiest**

buy   to get something by giving money for it (Kate needs money to *buy* a new rain hat.) **bought, buying**

C

candle   a stick of wax with a string in the middle that gives off light when it is lit with fire (When the lights went out, Grandfather lit a *candle*.)

careful   taking care; watching what you do (Be *careful* to do a good job on the math problems.)

chicken   a farm bird; a hen or rooster (Our *chickens* eat corn and live in the barn.)

chief   the top person; the person in charge of something (The *chief* of police told the other people what to do.)

circle   a line in the shape of a ring (The sun has the shape of a *circle*.)

clockmaker a person who makes and fixes clocks (The *clockmaker* fixed my clock so that it showed the right time.)

cloudy not sunny; full of clouds (We do not go swimming on *cloudy* or rainy days.) **cloudier, cloudiest**

cookie a small, thin, sweet cake (After school, we had milk and *cookies*.)

corner the place where two lines, sides, or walls meet (Most rooms have four *corners*.)

correct right; true; best (Mom showed James the *correct* way to cook pancakes.)

crayon a stick of colored wax that you can use for writing or drawing (Please color the sky on your paper with a blue *crayon*.)

create to make (With his new paints, my brother *created* a beautiful picture.) **created, creating**

D

darkness the state of having no light (There was no light in the room, and I could not see in the *darkness*.)

dinosaur a kind of animal that lived long, long ago (Some *dinosaurs* were much bigger than an elephant.)

donkey an animal like a small horse, but with longer ears (*Donkeys* make a loud hee-haw noise.)

doorknob the thing you turn to open a door (The *doorknob* would not turn.)

E

earth **1.** the planet where we all live (Some planes can fly all the way around the *earth*.) **2.** dirt; the ground (Lee covered the seeds with *earth*.)

eye the part of your body you use to see (If you put your hands over your *eyes*, you cannot see.)

F

fact a thing that is true (It is a *fact* that most birds can fly.)

favorite liked the best (Apples and oranges are Billy's *favorite* foods.)

field land with no trees, or just a few trees (It is safest to fly a kite in a *field*.)

flight 1. the act of flying through the air (The bird went many miles during its *flight*.) 2. a set of stairs (To get to the top floor of our house, you must climb two *flights* of stairs.)

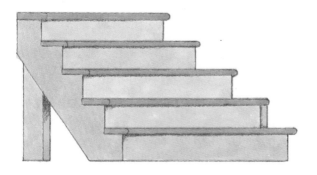

follow to come after (I know the way to go, so you can *follow* me.)

frighten to make afraid (Loud noises *frighten* some people.)

fuzzy 1. not sharp; not clear; blurred (Kim cannot see who is in the picture because it is *fuzzy*.) 2. covered with hair or fur (Peter has a soft, *fuzzy* teddy bear.)

G

giant a make-believe person who is very, very big (The *giant* did not fit in the tiny house.)

grind to crush into tiny bits (Our back teeth *grind* the food we eat.) **ground, grinding**

grumble to talk in a low voice about things that are not good; to complain (Sasha *grumbled* about having to feed the dog.) **grumbled, grumbling**

H

habit a thing you do over and over (It is a good *habit* to look both ways before you cross the street.)

hammer **1.** a tool to hit nails with (I pounded the nail with the *hammer*.) **2.** to hit something with a hammer (Susie *hammered* the nail.)

happily in a happy way (Jack smiled *happily*.)

hardly only just; barely (The shelf was so high that Marvin could *hardly* reach it.)

healthy not sick; well (Do you feel sick, or do you feel *healthy?*) **healthier, healthiest**

hear to pick up a sound with your ear (I cannot *hear* the bird singing.) **heard, hearing**

heard See **hear.**

heart the part of the body that moves the blood around (You can put your hand on your chest and feel your *heart* beat.)

heaviest See **heavy.**

heavy hard to pick up; having a lot of weight (A big rock is very *heavy*.) **heavier, heaviest**

helicopter a kind of airplane with no real wings. Blades on the top turn and move the helicopter up into the air. (A *helicopter* does not need a runway to land or to take off.)

high **1.** far up above the ground (The clouds were *high* in the sky.) **2.** very large in amount (Ruth got a *high* grade on the math test.) **higher, highest**

hour a part of time made up of 60 minutes (At school, we have an *hour* for lunch and play.)

hourglass an old kind of clock that uses falling sand to mark passing time (An *hourglass* is fat on the top and bottom, but very thin in the middle.)

hungrily in a manner that is hungry; in a way that shows a need for food (We ate the bread *hungrily*.)

husband a man who has a wife (Mr. Higgins is the *husband* of Mrs. Higgins.)

I

imagine to think about; to have a picture of something in your mind (I have never seen a whale, but I can *imagine* what one looks like.) **imagined, imagining**

important meaning a lot; worth a lot (It is *important* for you to know how to read.)

J

jungle a hot, damp place with many trees, bushes, and vines (Many pretty birds live in the *jungle*.)

K

kettle a pot or pan (On the stove, there was hot water in the *kettle*.)

L

large big; great (A mouse is a small animal, but a horse is a *large* one.) **larger, largest**

lazily in a way that is slow-moving and not wanting to work hard (When I try to get my brother out of bed, he just yawns *lazily*.)

learn to get to know; to find out (When did Luke *learn* how to roller-skate?)

lettuce a plant with big green leaves that are good to eat (Rabbits and people both like to eat *lettuce*.)

lion   a strong, large animal from Africa. It looks like a very big cat.

loose   able to move; not tight; not held down (The shoe was *loose*, so it fell off my foot.) **looser, loosest**

lose   not to have any longer; not to keep (I sometimes *lose* my toy boats when they go down the river.) **lost, losing**

lost   See **lose.**

loud   making a great noise (The music was so *loud* it hurt our ears.) **louder, loudest**

measure   to find the size of something (Molly uses her ruler to *measure* inches.)

million   one thousand thousand; very, very many (There are *millions* of leaves on the trees in the forest.)

molt   to drop old feathers before new ones grow (Many birds *molt* in the spring.)

money   coins or paper you can use to buy things (Lizzy went to the store and got oranges with her *money*.)

monkey   an animal with hair on its body and with hands that can hold things (Many *monkeys* have long tails.)

noisy   making a lot of loud sounds (When the baby bangs the pans on the floor, it is very *noisy*.) **noisier, noisiest**

none   not any (After Ann ate the last apple, there were *none* left.)

notice   to see; to pay attention to (Susan *noticed* the flowers in the garden.)

O

ocean   the very large body of water that covers much of the earth

o'clock   time on the clock (Harold gets up every day at seven *o'clock.*)

often   many times   (I *often* get my feet wet when it rains.)

once   one time; **at once**   at the same time   (Our teacher cannot hear what we are saying if we all talk *at once.*)

only   nothing else   (*Only* cats can purr.)

open   to move or change something so that it is not shut   (*Open* the window.)

P

paste   **1.** glue; a wet mix that you can use to stick things together   (The white *paste* sticks to my fingers.)   **2.** to stick things together using paste   (If the stamp falls off your letter, *paste* it back on.)
pasted, pasting

pencil   a tool to write or draw with   (Use your *pencil* to write on the paper.)

piece   a part or bit of something   (This puzzle has ten *pieces.*)

pillow   a bag filled with feathers or something else that is soft. You put your head on it for sleeping.   (There was a big *pillow* on the bed.)

pocket   a small place in clothing where you can put things   (Freddy hid the penny in his shirt *pocket.*)

polar bear   a big white bear that lives where it is very cold   (*Polar bears* live near the North Pole.)

police   the men and women who make sure that people obey the laws   (The *police* caught the speeding car.)

present something a person gives to another; a gift (Mom gave me a nice *present* on my birthday.)

problem something that needs to be fixed or worked out (I have a *problem:* my glasses are lost.)

promise to say that you will do something (Luke always does anything he *promises* to.) **promised, promising**

prove to show that something is true (I will *prove* that I can hop 100 times by doing it for you to see.) **proved, proving**

pumpkin a fruit that is big, round, orange, and good to cook and eat (Aunt Maria made a pie from a *pumpkin* from the garden.)

Q

quarter a coin that is worth 25 pennies (I must pay a *quarter* for the orange.)

quiet not making noise (A whisper is very *quiet.*)

quietly in a way that does not make noise (When I do not want to wake my mom, I play *quietly.*)

R

remember not to forget; to think again about something (Every day Lee *remembers* to lock the door.)

repay to pay back (Carlos gave me money for my lunch and I have to *repay* him.)

rescue to save from harm or danger (Jake *rescued* the baby bird that had fallen from the tree.)

rooster a male chicken; a farm bird (Three hens and one *rooster* lived in the barn.)

S

sad not happy (Do you ever cry when you are *sad?*)
sadder, saddest

scissors a tool used for cutting (Mark cut the paper with his *scissors.*)

shade a place with no sun; a dark spot (It was cool in the *shade* under the tree.)

shadow the dark place, or shade, made when the sun cannot shine through something (The umbrella blocked the sun and made a *shadow* on the sand.)

shine to send out light; to be bright (I love warm days when the sun *shines.*) **shined** (or **shone), shining**

should ought to (What *should* you do if you get lost?)

shovel a tool for digging (To dig a big hole, we need a *shovel.*)

softly in a low voice; quietly (Grandpa sang *softly* to the baby.)

somebody someone; a person (George wants *somebody* to help him.)

special one kind; not the same as everything else (My dog is my *special* friend.)

splendid very fine; very good (The fur coat was *splendid.*)

stairs steps that you go up or down (Peter climbed the *stairs* to the attic.)

storyteller someone who tells stories (We went to hear the *storyteller.*)

sugar a sweet food (Cakes and cookies are made with *sugar.*)

sundial a kind of old clock that uses shadows to mark the hours (A *sundial* works only when the sun shines.)

sunrise the time when the sun is just coming up

sure knowing without doubt (You can be *sure* the sun will come up every day.)

T

tall high (My father is six feet *tall*, and my uncle is even *taller*.) **taller, tallest**

teeth See **tooth.**

thick fat; not thin (That big, heavy book is very *thick*.) **thicker, thickest**

though in spite of the fact that (Even *though* I like most sports, I don't like football.)

tiny very small (The seed was so *tiny* that it was hard to see.)

together with each other; at the same time (Tomás and his dad read books *together*.)

tongue the part of your body you use to talk with and to taste food with (The cat licked the milk with its *tongue*.)

tonight this night (We will go to the movies *tonight*.)

tooth a hard bone in your mouth that you use for biting (A rat's *tooth* is sharp.)
pl. **teeth**

toward to; in the direction of (Max walked *toward* the top of the hill.)

trouble a problem; a time when something is wrong (People in *trouble* need help.)

turnip a plant with a big round root that is good for eating (My Uncle Lee cooks soup made of *turnip*.)

tusk   a long, sharp tooth that sticks far out of the mouth (Elephants have two *tusks*.)

u

until   up to the time when (My baby sister ate in a high chair *until* she was one year old.)

v

vegetable   a plant with parts that are good to eat (Peas, corn, and beets are *vegetables*.)

village   a very little town (There are five houses and one store in our *village*.)

w

walnut   a nut with a round, bumpy shell (The cake has *walnuts* in it.)

walrus   a big animal that lives in the sea in cold places (The *walrus* is slow on land but fast in water.)

whale   an animal that looks like a very big fish and lives in the sea (*Whales* swim like fish, but they must breathe air.)

whistle   to make a high, sharp sound (When the train gets near our town, we hear it *whistle*.)

wiggle   to move a little, side to side (Molly can *wiggle* her nose.) **wiggled, wiggling**

wonderful   great or fine (Max had a *wonderful* time at the zoo.)

worry   not to feel easy; to be troubled (When I am late, my dad *worries* about me.) **worried, worrying**

y

young   not old (Those small trees are very *young*.) **younger, youngest**

Cover/Cluster Openers   **Design:** Studio Goodwin-Sturges.   **Illustration:** Holly Berry.   **Calligraphy:** Colleen.

Editorial   **Book Editor:** Laura A. Tills.   **Senior Editor:** Susan D. Paro.   **Editorial Services:** Marianna Frew Palmer, K. Kirschbaum Harvie.   **Permissions Editor:** Dorothy Burns McLeod.
Design   **Series:** Leslie Dews.   **Book:** Ellen Coolidge, Ingrid Cooper.
Production   Mary Hunter.

Illustration   **10–14:** Tomie de Paola, copyright © 1976, from *The Giants' Farm,* with permission. **16–17:** Mary Szilagyi. **18–26:** Margot Zemach. **28–30:** Slug Signorino. **34–36:** Misty G. McArthur. **38–44:** Frank Asch, copyright © 1985, from *Bear Shadow,* with permission. **46–50:** Gary Fujiwara. **52–66:** Pamela R. Levy. **70–71:** G. Brian Karas. **72–80:** Babette Cole. **82–83:** Holly Berry. **89–96:** Irene Trivas. **100–110:** William C. Bell. **114–117:** Dorothea R. Sierra. **119–137:** Lynn Sweat, copyright © 1976, from *Good Work, Amelia Bedelia,* with permission. **140–148:** Ellen Weiss, copyright © 1976, from *Heather's Feathers,* with permission. **154–164:** Irene Trivas. **168–172:** Jamichael Henterly. **174–178:** Cyndy Patrick. **180–190:** Leslie Evans. **194–201:** Cathie Bleck. **203–207:** Carol M. Vidinghoff. **208:** Pete Whitehead. **212–218:** Stephen Moscowitz. **220–224:** Dorothea R. Sierra. **226–244:** Marc Simont, copyright © 1978, from *Nate the Great and the Sticky Case,* with permission. **242–253:** Jan Pyk.

Photography   **84:** Alan Mercer (Stock Boston). **85:** *t,* Frank Siteman (Stock Boston); *bl,* Michael and Barbara Reed (Animals Animals); *br,* David C. Bitters (The Picture Cube). **86:** *tl,* © Brent Jones; *tr,* Jean Wentworth (The Picture Cube); *c,* Owen Franken (Stock Boston). **87:** *t,* Ernest Wilkenson (Animals Animals); *c,* Owen Franken (Stock Boston); *b,* Dan McCoy (Rainbow). **112–113:** Jeffrey Coolidge © D.C. Heath. **114:** *t,* Photo of Ringling Brothers clown © by Randa Bishop (Black Star); *b,* © Lou Jones. **115:** F.W. Binzen (Photo Researchers); *tr,* Nance S. Trueworthy; *bl,* Erika Stone; *br,* Nance S. Trueworthy. **116:** Hank Morgan (Rainbow). **117:** *l,* David C. Bitters (The Picture Cube); *tr,* Nance S. Trueworthy; *br,* R. Hutchings (Photo Researchers). **150:** *t,* Richard Kolar (Animals Animals); *c,* Alan D. Carey; *b,* Anthony Bannister (Animals Animals). **151:** *t,* Dallas and John Heaton (Stock Shop); *c,* John Messineo; *b,* Suen-o Lindblad (Photo Researchers). **152:** *t,* J.D. Cunningham (Visuals Unlimited); *b,* © Kennan Ward. **174:** David and Linda Phillips. **175:** Tom McHugh (Photo Researchers). **176:** David S. Strickler (The Picture Cube). **177:** © Jeffrey L. Rotman. **178:** © Brent Jones.
Photo Coordinator: Connie Komack.   **Photo Research:** Martha Friedman.   **Photo Styling:** Nanci Lindholm.